Dr John Allwork

C# and .NET Programming for Engineers

C# and .NET Programming for Engineers

Dr John Allwork

Elektor International Media BV
Postbus 11
6114 ZG Susteren
The Netherlands

British Library Cataloguing in Publication Data
A catalogue record for this book is available from the British Library

ISBN 978-0-905705-81-1

Prepress production: Autronic, Blaricum
First published in the United Kingdom 2009
Second edition November 2009
Printed in the Netherlands by Wilco, Amersfoort
© Elektor International Media BV 2009

099005-UK

Contents

6

About the Author

John Allwork was born in 1950 in Kent, England and became interested in electronics and engineering at school. He went to Sheffield University on their BEng Electrical and Electronic Engineering course. There he developed an interest in computers and continued his education on an MSc course in Digital Electronics and Communication at UMIST. After two years working for ICL as design, commissioning and test Engineer he returned to UMIST where he graduated with a PhD in 'Design and Development of Microprocessor systems'

He worked for several years in technical support and as manager in electronics distribution, working closely with Intel Application Engineers and followed this with design work on the Inmos Transputer systems.

He has been a lecturer at Manchester Metropolitan University in the Engineering and Technology Department since 1991.

His interests apart from electronics include skiing, walking and spending time on his allotment or on his narrowboat.

Introduction

This book is aimed at Engineers and Scientists who have an interest in interfacing hardware to a PC, in particular using the USB port and controlling or display data using a graphical user interface. However it will also be useful for those who want to learn about the .NET environment and C# programming and covers computer concepts such as object oriented programming, threading and databases.

Although it assumes a little knowledge of programming it starts from the basics and covers the Visual Studio development environment, the .NET framework and C# programming language from data types and program flow to more advanced concepts such as object oriented programming.

It continues with program debugging, file handling, databases, threading, internet communication using TCP/IP and UDP and graphs and plotting before moving to hardware interfacing using serial and parallel ports and the USB port. It includes a hardware design for a simple oscilloscope via the parallel port and interfacing to analogue and digital I/O using the USB port.

It is complete with many program examples, self assessment exercises and links to supporting videos. Full program examples are available, as is support for University lecturers in the form of PowerPoint presentations for most chapters.

I do not pretend to know all there is about C# and the .NET framework. I have a background in hardware design and writing software to control it. There may be mistakes in the book at which programmers may be offended and I am sure there are better ways to write some of the code, but I have written and tried all the examples and know they work. I hope the examples will spur you on to find solutions to your own problems. Should you need more information then please try the on-line help and the Microsoft forums. There are plenty of programmers out there willing to help solve your problems, sometimes extremely quickly.

I wish to thank my friends and colleagues at Manchester Metropolitan University for encouraging me and checking the manuscript, especially Dr Hugh Frost, Dr George South and Dr Nader Anani; my students who have unwittingly helped me clarify and enhance the book; Matt Howlett from NPlot for permission to use their images; Don Powrie from DLP Design, Inc. for help and clarification of the USB module protocol and hardware interfacing and the many anonymous people on the internet, forums, blogs and websites who have answered many questions, not just my own – keep up the good work. Not least of all I would like to thank my wife for supporting me throughout.

And of course you for buying the book!

Conventions used in this book

A few conventions used in the book, used mainly to distinguish normal text from C# code and program output.

Normal text	Times New Roman - Used for plain text
Program code	Arial - C# source code and snippets of code
`Program output`	`Courier New` – program output in MSDOS window

I have also used the 'greater than' symbol to indicate that the reader should follow a sequence of commands, such as File> New Project > Windows application.

1 The Visual Studio C# Environment

1.1 Introduction

C# is a modern programming language and the Visual Studio environment lets you write graphical user based programs for Windows. The .NET framework provides extensive interface libraries. Programs written in C# can be used alongside programs written in VB.NET and J# code. The programs are compiled to an intermediate language, or common language runtime CLR, which is then run on the specific computer, see figure 1.1. This makes your C# programs platform independent but of course we will be dealing solely with writing programs for the PC.

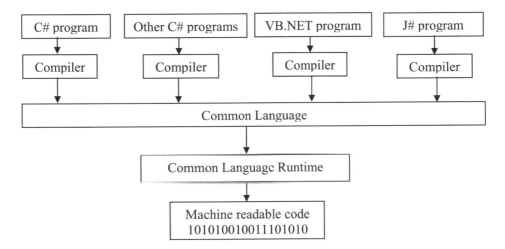

Figure 1.1 .NET common language operation

This design means that C# programs run slower than truly compiled programs such as C++, but the benefits outweigh the disadvantages. The .NET framework also provides access to programs that execute outside the framework, in our case access to hardware ports using the P/Invoke feature. The current version of the .NET framework is 3.5.

1.2 Obtaining the C# software

Visual C# is part of the Visual Studio suite of software and the Express Edition can be downloaded for free from the Microsoft web site. The Express Edition is ideal for learning the language and contains everything we shall need. The software is available at

http://www.microsoft.com/express/download/default.aspx

Choose 'download and install' answer any questions and install SQL 2008 if you want to use databases. You are reminded to register, but it's an easy process and a good idea. You can do this from the Help > Register Product menu within Visual Studio.

The Microsoft forums are a good place to go for help and if you get stuck there's help at: http://forums.microsoft.com/msdn:

MSDN Forums>Visual Studio Express Editions>Installing and registering.

There are plenty of videos available from Microsoft which are mentioned later.

1.3   The Visual Studio development environment

The development environment enables you to create, run and debug your program via a graphical user interface (GUI). When you run Visual Studio it starts with an introductory page, see figure 1.2. To start a new Windows project, select File> New Project and choose 'Windows application'. Give the project a name e.g. 'HelloWorld'.

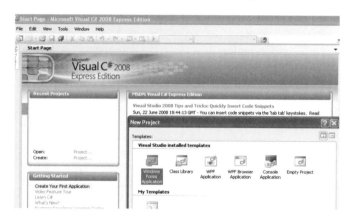

Figure 1.2 Visual Studio introductory page

Click OK to display the development environment, see figure 1.3.

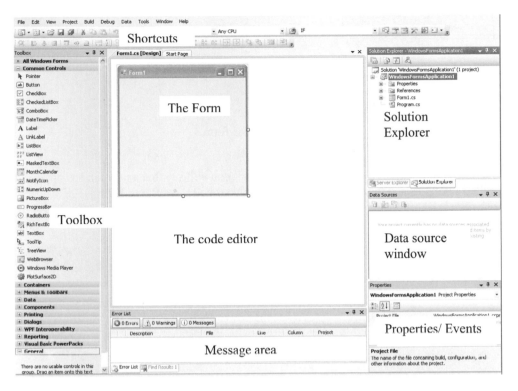

Figure 1.3 The C# development environment.

In the centre is the form where we will create our design by placing controls such as buttons, labels and text boxes, etc. Behind this is the editing area for our code. The Toolbox is on the left. The short-cut icons at the top; the Solution Explorer, Data Sources and Properties Windows are on the right and the error window at the bottom. The toolbox expands to show the controls when you click it. To display it permanently click the icon that looks like a drawing pin. If the toolbox or any of the other windows aren't displayed, select View> Toolbox (Properties Window, Task list etc.). The tabs above the form will display our code and other development windows. You can drag the windows around to create your own preferred layout.

1.3.1 The Form

This is the most important part of the GUI design, see figure 1.4. In development it is where the controls (buttons, labels, text boxes etc.) are placed. When the program runs, it is what the user finally sees and how they interact with your program.

Form1

Figure 1.4 The form.

1.3.2 The Code Editor.

Double click the form to display the code editor. You will see that a new tab has appeared called Form1.cs and this is where you will type your code, see figure 1.5.

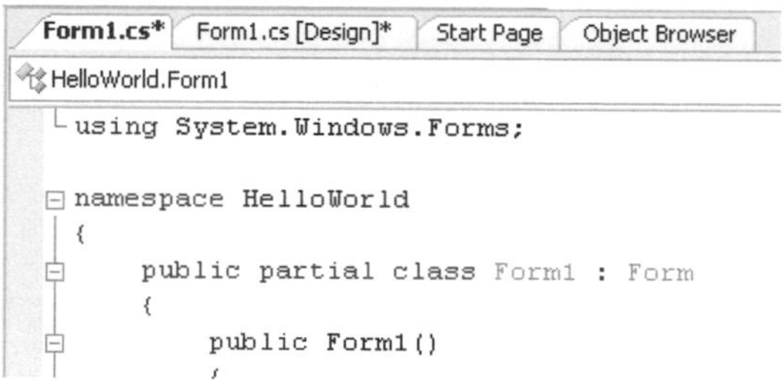
Form1.cs*
Form1.cs [Design]*
Start Page
Object Browser
HelloWorld.Form1
using System.Windows.Forms;
namespace HelloWorld
{
public partial class Form1 : Form
{
public Form1()

Figure1.5 The code editor

Notice that some code is already inserted for you, but you will still have to write the important parts!

Do not delete code that you have not typed as this will cause an error when you compile your code.

1.3.3 The Toolbox

The toolbox contains the controls we will use in our user interface, see figure 1.6.

Toolbox
All Windows Forms
Common Controls
Pointer
Button
CheckBox
CheckedListBox
ComboBox
DateTimePicker
Label
LinkLabel
ListBox

Figure 1.6 The Toolbox

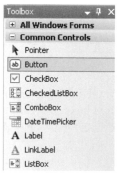

You can choose to hide the toolbox or display it permanently. If it is hidden, to display it just move the cursor over the Toolbox icon. In order to place a control on the form, simply click the control and drag it to the form.

The tools are grouped in similar functions; Common controls (buttons, labels, text boxes), Containers (forms, panels), Menus, Toolbars, etc. We shall introduce the controls as we need them. Note that you can only see the toolbox when the design tab is selected.

1.3.4 The Properties/Events window

All controls have their own properties. For example a button will have a certain position on the form (Top and Left), a size (Height and Width), Text and Font etc. They are all listed in the properties box. Figure 1.7 shows the Text property of a textBox highlighted. The order of the properties can be changed between alphabetical and categorized.

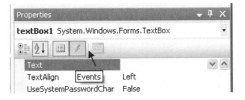

Figure 1.7 Button properties

Clicking the lightning bolt event icon shown in figure 1.7 will change the display to show the events for that control, e.g. Click or MouseHover. Figure 1.8 shows the Click event for the button selected. A short description of the event is displayed at the bottom of the properties window.

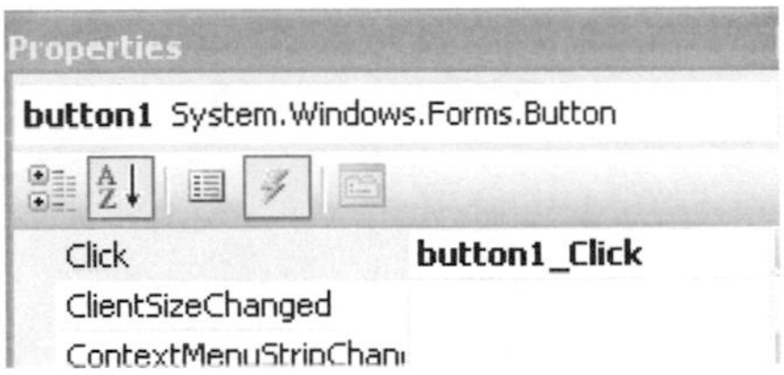

Figure 1.8 Control click event display

Clicking the list icon to the left of the event icon, will redisplay the properties list.

C# programs are event driven and can be generated by the user, your program or the operating system. The program responds to these events. Different controls have different events, for example an event can be generated when text is typed into a textbox but that can't happen with a button. We will look at events later, but common events are:

- Clicking a button (Click event),

- Typing a key on the keyboard (KeyDown and KeyUp or combined to make a KeyPress)
- Mouse events (MouseMove, MouseDown, MouseUp, MouseMove, MouseClick)

Event driven programs can be difficult to debug and we shall see how to debug our programs later.

As you write your programs, the editor's 'IntelliSense' will prompt you for possible entries. The dot notation is used to access the methods, properties and events, e.g. button.Height. We shall cover methods and events later. Figure 1.9 shows some of the entries that can follow the full stop after 'button1.' has been typed.

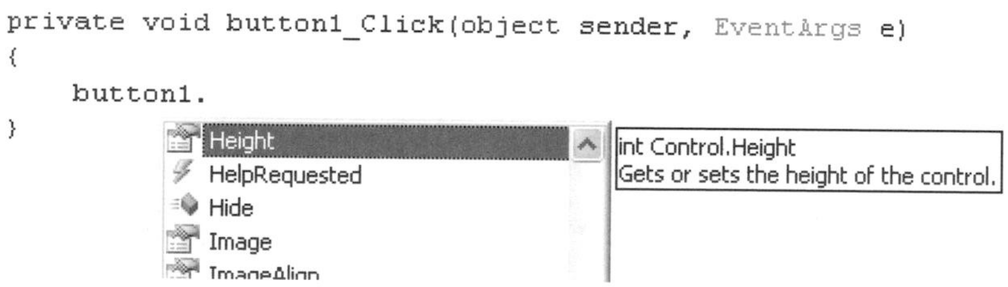

```
private void button1_Click(object sender, EventArgs e)
{
    button1.
}
```

Figure 1.9 IntelliSense prompt

To help you, different icons are used for a method (DrawToBitmap), a property (Enabled) and an event (EnabledChange), see figure 1.10.

DragOver
DrawToBitmap
Enabled
EnabledChanged

Figure 1.10 Method, Property and Event icons

1.4   Exercises

1.4.1   Your First C# Program

To introduce you to the simplest and most common controls, let's write a Windows program to display 'Hello World' on the screen. (The 'Hello World' is a common program used to introduce users to a new programming language)

1. Run Visual Studio C#, start a new Project (File>New Project), select Windows Application and rename it 'Hello world'. Choose the folder where you want you program to be saved.
2. Before continuing, save the project. Select File>Save All. Each project is saved in its own folder.

3. Display the form (click the form1.cs[Design] tab). Select a button control from the Toolbox>Common Controls (use View > Toolbox if it's not displayed) and place it on the form (either click and drag the control, or click the control and then click the form), see figure 1.11.

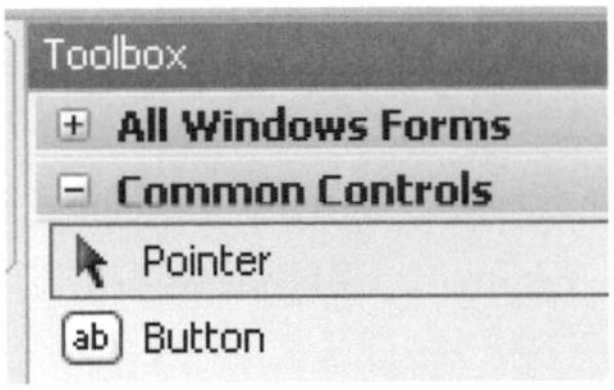

Figure 1.11 Button control.

This will place a button named 'Button1' on the form. Make it a sensible size.

4. Let's change the text on the button. Display the properties window if necessary (View> Properties Window), scroll to the Text property and type in 'Hello world', see figure 1.12. Select the properties list icon if necessary to display the properties

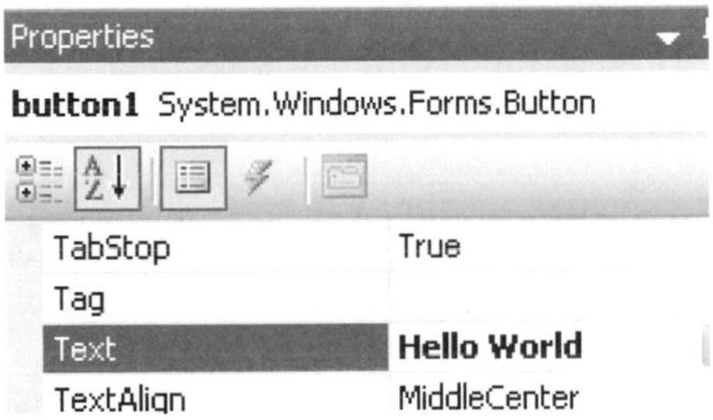

Figure 1.12 The Properties window

5. Select a TextBox from the Toolbox and place it on the form. Alignment lines appear so you can align the controls. Place the controls side by side. Text boxes are used to get data into and out of your program. This is where the message 'Hello world' will be displayed. It's currently blank.

6. Finally add one further control, a label. Click the label control and place it on the form above the others, and change its caption property to 'My First C# Program'.

Note how the size of the label automatically changes to fit the text. You may not want this, and of course this is a property that can be changed.

7. Your form should be similar to figure 1.13.

You can delete any control by clicking it to select the control and pressing the 'delete' key.

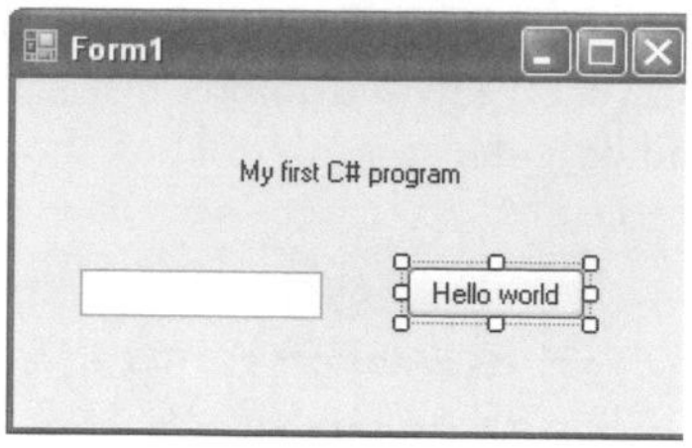

Figure 1.13 Hello world GUI

8. Familiarise yourself with moving controls around the form. Click and hold the mouse button and move the mouse to move controls around, or single click to select the controls and use the re-sizing controls; the squares around the object, see the button in figure 1.13.

9. At this stage it is possible to run the program. Before running it, save the program. Click File>Save All.

To run the program, click Debug>Start debugging, press the F5 function key, or click the ('play') green triangle. There are often different ways to do the same operation and you will find your own preferred shortcuts.

Your 'program' will be compiled and run. You can't do much yet. You can click the button and enter text in the text box, even though you haven't written any code yet. Close the program (Click **X** on Form1, choose Debug > Stop debugging or press shift-F5).

10. To write the code to display a message, double-click the 'Hello world' button, and between the curly brackets { } type:

```
textBox1.Text="Hello world";
```

This line of code changes the text in the textbox to 'Hello world'. Note that C# is case sensitive and as we have seen gives you hints and code completion as you type. It also highlights in different colours code meanings such as keywords and strings.

The complete code for the button click is:

```
private void button1_Click(object sender, EventArgs e)
{
    textBox1.Text = "Hello world";
}
```

Remember, some of this has been written for you. If you didn't type the code, don't delete it.

11. Save the project and run it (press F5). When the button is clicked, it should display 'Hello world' in the text box.

Congratulations, you have just written and executed your first C# program!

Save and close your application. Reload it and if the form doesn't display, click the form1.cs in the Solution Explorer, see section 1.5.

1.4.2   Properties

Now that you understand how to change the control's properties, try changing from within your program on the button click:

1. Change the label caption, e.g.:   Label1.Text = "new name";

2. Change the position of the button, label or textbox using 'Left' and 'Top' properties, say add 5 to each when the button is clicked and see how the textbox moves, e.g.

    Button1.Left = Button1.Left + 5;

3. Change the size of the label (Height and width), button caption, its colour (using System.Drawing.Color.Red) or other properties, e.g.

    Label1.Height = Label1.Height + 34;

4. More button properties:
The Font property is used to change button's text. You can change the font, style, size, colour and effects. The BackColor and ForeColor properties change the colours and you can choose from System (Windows), Web or Custom colours. You can also choose an image to display on your button and hence could have any design on your button.

5. Exit program
There are two ways you can close your program. You can just exit from the application, or you can close the form. If your application has more than one form it will exit when you close the main form.

Add two buttons to your form and change their Name property to 'btnClose' and 'btnExit'. Add the following code for them respectively:

    this.Close( ) ;   and   Application.Exit( );

We shall explain what is meant by 'this' later, but here it means the form itself.
Now you can close your program by clicking a button.

1.5   Solution Explorer

Your code and Graphical User Interface (GUI) form design are combined into a project. The Solution Explorer shows how these are combined. In our first program we only have one form and its code, but there could be multiple forms.

My Solution Explorer looks like figure 1.14:

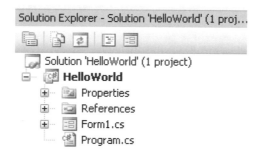

Figure 1.14 Solution Explorer

Hint: If the development environment isn't displaying what you need, try clicking within the Solution Explorer or clicking its icons.

1.6   Program execution.

If you look in your folder, you will see that the program EXE file size is about 20kb. This is not the whole program. Your program will only run on another computer if it has the .NET framework installed. As we have mentioned, the C# compiler only compiles to intermediate code, which then runs under the .NET framework. This means it does run slower than truly compiled languages, but has the advantage that programs from different languages can be combined.

1.7   Number conversion.

The text in a Text box is held as a 'string' data type. If you want to deal with numbers, you have to convert from a number to a string and vice versa. We will see this in more detail later, but if you want to try it now, to convert to a string to display a number we use .ToString( ). Typical examples are:

```
// this is a comment - declare and initialise an integer number
int integerNumber = 42;

// declare and initialise a real number
double realNumber = 3.14159;

// convert integer to string and display
```

```
textBox1.Text = integerNo.ToString( ) ;

// convert real number and display
textBox1.Text = realNumber.ToString( ) ;
```

The above code declares an integer and a floating point number and converts them both to strings and displays them in a text box. The double-slash is a comment line.

We may need to convert numbers which have been typed into a textBox (i.e. a string) to an integer or floating point number. To do this we use the Parse command, for example Int32.Parse( ) or float.Parse( ), as follows:

```
// read a string and convert it to an integer
// declare an integer, i
int i;
// read textBox, convert to integer
i = Int32.Parse(textBox1.Text);
// square number and write back
textBox1.Text = (i * i).ToString( );

// read a string and convert it to a floating point number
// declare a realNumber
double realNumber;
// read text box and convert to floating point number
realNumber = float.Parse(textBox1.Text);
// square number and write back
textBox1.Text = (i * i).ToString();
```

Obviously if you try converting a floating point number to an integer you will get an error. We shall see how we deal with errors later.

1.8   Exercise: Simple calculator

We shall demonstrate the number and string conversions using a simple calculator. It will have two text boxes for the numbers and one for the result. We shall provide the basic mathematical functions.

Start a new application (File>New Project > Windows application, give it a suitable name).
Place three text boxes on the form, one for each of the two numbers to be calculated and one for the result. In this example we will use the default names for the controls.

Add four buttons, change the Text on each to '+', '-', '*', and '/'. Change the font size so the text looks good. Finally add an 'equals' label.

Your form should look like the example in figure 1.15.

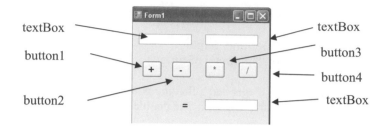

Figure 1.15 Calculator GUI design

The diagram has been labelled so you know which control is which. Later on we will discuss naming conventions and suggest sensible names so the control's function is obvious.

Double-click the 'add' button and change the code for the button click event to the following:

```
private void button1_Click(object sender, EventArgs e)
{
    textBox3.Text = (double.Parse(textBox1.Text) +
                        double.Parse(textBox2.Text)).ToString( );
}
```

The calculation is all in one line of code so we don't have to declare any variables. The text box values are read and converted to floating point double precision numbers, added together, converted back to a string and placed in textBox3.

Save your project and run the program. Enter some numbers in the text boxes and see if it adds the numbers correctly.

We can declare the variables if we want to. We will look at declaring variables later, but you can try the following code for the subtract button:

```
private void button2_Click(object sender, EventArgs e)
{
    double fpNumber1, fpNumber2;
    fpNumber1 = double.Parse(textBox1.Text);
    fpNumber2 = double.Parse(textBox2.Text);
    textBox3.Text = (fpNumber1 - fpNumber2).ToString( );
}
```

Self Assessment Exercises

Video support.

1) Microsoft has a supporting installation and introductory video at:

26

http://msdn.microsoft.com/en-us/beginner/bb964631.aspx

This covers installation and many Visual C# 2008 features, including debugging and database access, so you might want to stop at 'Errors and Debugging' (after about 23 minutes) and return to it later.

2) Watch the 'Getting Started' and 'Creating a User Interface' pointed to by Elektor's web site.

3) Expand the Calculator program for the multiply and divide buttons yourself and check your calculator works.

4) Take a look at the various ways of getting help.

- o Select a control and press the F1 function key
- o Click Help > Search and type in a search item
- o Click Help > How do I? and look at the options
- o Visit the Microsoft Developer Network Library at:
    http://msdn2.microsoft.com/en-us/library/default.aspx

Summary

This chapter has introduced the .NET framework, Visual Studio development environment and C# programming language. The .NET framework is a collection of libraries that we will use form our C# program.

The development environment windows have been seen: the form where the user interface design is created; the code window; the solution explorer, properties and events windows and the toolbox. We have used common controls such as buttons, labels and the textbox. Some of the properties and events of these common controls have been used.

We have written a simple program to display a message. We have seen how numbers are converted to strings and we have written a basic calculator program.

2 Common controls, properties and events

2.1 Introduction

We have seen the most commonly used controls; the button and textbox and some of their events. In this chapter we shall look at these controls in more detail and then look at more of the other common controls and their properties and events.

2.2 The Button   button1

The button's main properties are its appearance – Color, Image and Text; its behaviour – Enabled or Visible and its design - Name, Location and Size. Note the American spelling is used and remember in our programs the properties are case sensitive.

An important and useful property is the Tag property. This is free for you to use and can contain any type of information All controls have a Tag property and if you want to use it you need to set the data type you want before you use it. We shall see how to use this later.

The button's main event is (button) Click, but it has Mouse events such as MouseEnter, MouseHover, MouseMove and MouseLeave. It also has events such as DragDrop and DragEnter to allow dragging and dropping of items, and surprisingly it also has keyboard events such as KeyDown and KeyPress.

2.3 The TextBox   abl TextBox

Looking at the TextBox will give us a chance to see how we deal with text generally. The main properties are similar to the button (appearance, behaviour and design), but it also has text control properties.

The Text property contains all the text in the TextBox. A textbox can have single or multiple lines which is set by the MultiLine property. The text can be ReadOnly and there are many other properties including WordWrap and AutoComplete.

These can all be seen in the properties box, see figure 2.1.

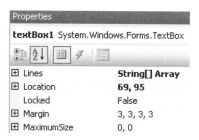

Figure 2.1 TextBox properties

The Textbox has the mouse and drag events mentioned, but the keyboard events are more relevant for this control. They are TextChanged, KeyDown, KeyUp and KeyPress (a KeyDown followed by KeyUp).

The individual keys typed can be checked, see the Self Assessment exercises for more details.

2.3.1 Dealing with text in a TextBox

The text is held in the Lines property. To see this and add some text, place a textbox on the form and look at the lines property in the Properties window. Remember, if this window isn't displayed, use View > Property Window to display it. Scroll to the Lines property, it looks like figure 2.2.

Figure 2.2 The TextBox lines property

It's a String array, but don't worry about this now; we shall cover arrays later on.

Click the box with the three dots (ellipses) to display a dialog box where the text required in each of the lines of the textbox can be added, see figure 2.3.

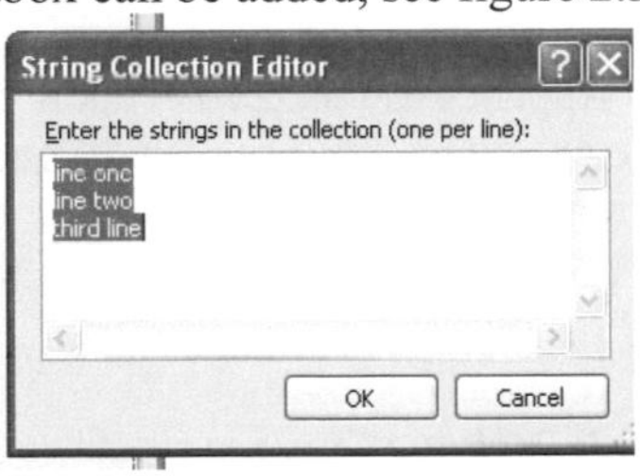

Figure 2.3 Entering text for a TextBox

Enter some lines of text and look at the Text property. It will be similar to figure 2.4.

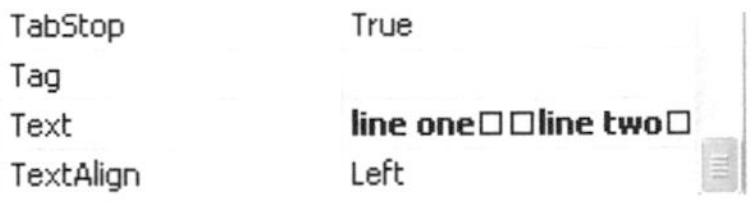

TabStop	True
Tag	
Text	**line one□□line two□**
TextAlign	Left

Figure 2.4 TextBox multiple lines of text

When the program runs, the text is displayed all on one line as shown in figure 2.5.

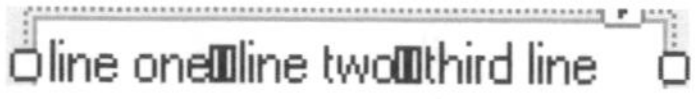

Figure 2.5 TextBox with single line text

The default is for a single line of text and the squares represent the carriage return and line feed characters which would normally put the text on different lines. If you want multiple lines of text, set the MultiLine property true. If you do this the text appears on individual lines as shown in figure 2.6.

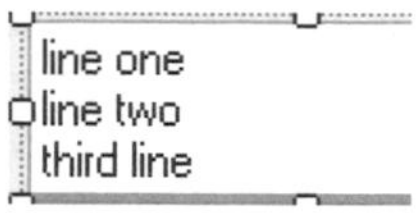

Figure 2.6 TextBox with multiple lines of text

If the number of lines becomes too big for the textbox, horizontal and vertical scrollbars can also be displayed by selecting from the properties.

All the lines of text can be read in one go using the Text property (textBox1.Text). Individual lines can be read using the Lines[ ] property as follows:

    textBox1.Lines[0]

Note that Lines[0] is the first line.

To add lines to the TextBox, 'AppendText' is used. This is called a method. Controls like buttons and textboxes are objects and have Properties, Events and Methods. We have seen properties and events; a method is code that we call to do some work for us. In this case add text into the textbox. We shall more of this later and write our own. To add text use:

    textBox1.AppendText("new text");

This just appends text onto the last line and does not create a new line. To add text on to a new line, add the escape characters \r\n (meaning return and new line) as follows:

    textBox1.AppendText("\r\nnew last line");

The total number of lines in the TextBox can be found with the Length property:

    textBox1.Lines.Length;

So you can always access the last line with the code:

    textBox1.Lines[textBox1.Lines.Length-1];

Remember, data in a textbox is held as a string and you may have to convert it to a form you need.

2.4   The ListBox control   ListBox

The List Box control contains a scrollable list of items that can be selected but not altered by the user (i.e. accessible only from within the program).

Items are added at design time in the same way as with a TextBox, using Items > Collection, and of course the items can be added and removed by your program.

If you want to allow your user to select more than one item choose MultiSimple, or MultiExtended from the SelectionMode property. The first allows multiple selections but the second also allows use of control and shift to select multiple items.

As with the textbox, individual lines are addressed using listBox.Items[x], where Items[0] is the first line. List box items are added using the code:

```
listBox1.Items.Add("string");
```

String conversion is done automatically, so you can add strings, integers, floating point numbers etc. You can have:

```
listBox1.Items.Add(34);      // number 34
listBox1.Items.Add("234"); // text 234
double f = 3.1415;
listBox1.Items.Add(f);              // floating point
```

You can try this now. Place a List Box on your form and add the above code to a button click code. Run the program and confirm that the items are added to the List Box every time the button is clicked.

You can insert items at a specific position using the Insert method:

```
listBox1.Items.Insert (lineNo, "insertMe");
```

You can remove them using the Remove method:

```
listBox1.Remove("string");          // remove the first occurrence of "string"
```

Or you can remove items at a specific line number using the RemoveAt method:

```
listBox1.RemoveAt(lineNo);
```

You can also clear the list box:

```
listBox1.Clear();
```

You can see the listBox has many methods.

Eventually the item added is at the bottom and scroll bars appear. However the item just added isn't visible – the user has to scroll to see it. If you want to display the last item added you can use the following code:

```
listBox1.SelectedIndex = listBox1.Items.Count-1;
```

If you want the scroll bars to be permanent, set the ScrollBarsAlwaysVisible property to true.

To identify the selected item use the SelectedItem property:

```
listBox1.SelectedItem
```

2.5   The CheckedListBox

The Checked List Box performs a similar operation to the list box, but with a check box beside each item.

The default event for both the list box and checked list box is SelectedIndexChanged which occurs when the user selects an item.

2.6   The CheckBox ☐ checkBox1

The check box is used to select one or many items from a selection. The main property is of course if it is checked or not. (CheckBox1.Checked = True or False).

Its main event occurs when its state is changed, CheckedChanged.

You may need to group checkboxes together. To do this place them within a contatiner such as a Panel, GroupBox or TabControl

2.7   The RadioButton ○ radioButton2

Radio buttons are used when only one item from a list needs to be (or can only be) selected, e.g. first year, second year or third year. Selecting one will automatically switch the others off.

Should you need to have more than one group, for instance to select a course as well as a year, you need to put the radio buttons in separate containers, such as a panel or a GroupBox. We'll look at containers later.

The text beside a radio button is set by its text property and it has a checked property (true or false) which can be set or tested by the program.

Double-clicking the radio button will take you to the CheckedChanged event. You can check the radio button's checked state using the code:

```
if (radioButton1.Checked)
        { doSomething( ); }
```

2.8   The NumericUpDown control

If you want a user to enter a number you code use a text box, but then you will have to check the user enter a properly formatted number and request correct input if the input is wrong. The NumericUpDown control ensures your user can only enter numbers within a certain range. It displays a number with up and down buttons to change the number. The user can also type in the required number, but if it is out of range, the control will limit the number.

The minimum and maximum values the control will display are set by the Minimum and Maximum properties, and the current value is in the Value property.

The default event for the NumericUpDown is ValueChanged. This event will be triggered every time the value is incremented or decremented (which may not be what you want).

2.9   Displaying Images – the PictureBox control

The PictureBox control is used to display an image. To choose the picture for the image, select the image property, click the ellipses (…) and browse for the image you want displayed. You can choose from a wide range of file formats including gif, jpg, bmp, or png. You can also display animated gifs.

The PictureBox tasks can be displayed by clicking the arrow icon at the top right hand corner of the picture, see figure 2.7. The picture can be shown in Normal, StretchImage, AutoSize, CenterImage and Zoom modes.

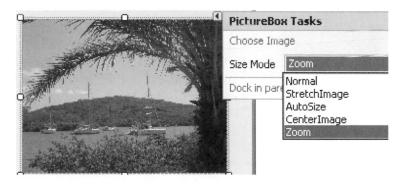

Figure 2.7 PictureBox Tasks.

If you want to select the picture to be displayed from a file, set the Image property using the Image.FromFile() method as follows:

```
pictureBox1.Image = Image.FromFile("filename");
```

2.10   Focus and TabIndex

This is good point to mention focus. When a user clicks on a control it becomes the active control and is said to 'gain focus'. An Enter event also occurs. When a user clicks away from a control, it loses focus and a Leave event occurs. Of course don't have to write any code for these events. The order in which the controls gain focus when the user uses the tab key to move around the form's items is controlled by the TabIndex property.

2.11   Even more controls.

Some other controls you might like to look at are listed here. We may encounter some of these later. You will have used most of these in your windows applications, they are:

- Combo Box – a drop down list of selectable items
- DateTimePicker – to select a date and time
- MonthCalendar - to select a month
- ProgressBar – indicating progress
- WebBrowser
- Print controls

2.12   Container controls toolbox

You can see we might want to group items together on a form and the containers control group do that for you. The most common ones (apart from the form) are the Panel and the GroupBox. The Panel is a simplified version of the Group Box (it doesn't have border or a caption for instance). Containers can hold other containers. The container controls panel is shown in figure 2.8:

Figure 2.8. The Containers ToolBox

To see this working, place a Group Box on the form, then select a Checkbox and drag it over the Group Box. Now try moving the Group Box and notice that the Checkbox moves with it. We will use various containers in the design exercise in the next section.

2.13 Listing controls

Every object you place on a form is recorded in the form's Controls property. The first object is Controls[0], the second Controls[1], etc. The total number of objects on the form is given by Controls.Count.

Every control has a .ToString( ) method, which returns a string of information about the object. You can see all the names of the controls on a form with the following code. Place a button and a selection of controls on a form and add the following code for the button click:

```
for (int i = 0; i<this.Controls.Count; i++)
{
    MessageBox.Show("Control number "+i.ToString( ) + " is called" +
        this.Controls[i].Name);
}
```

The keyword 'this' refers to the current object, in this case the form.

2.14 Exercise: Dating registration form

Let's create a registration form which might be used for a dating agency. We will just consider the design and controls, we won't write any code for this.

The form will have a tab control to select different pages for name, address and details of the person they would like to meet (WLTM).

On the Name tab, there will be TextBoxes for First name and Last Name, radio buttons to select gender (M or F) and a NumericUpDown control to select your age.

The Address tab will have TextBoxes for address and a scrollable list box to select a country (UK, Europe, USA, other).

The WLTM Details tab will have the following controls:
A panel control containing:
A check box to select common interests (sports, pub, walking, dining out).
Radio buttons to select age range of the person you would like to meet (range 18-25, 26-39, 40-59, 60+).

Start a new project, windows application and call it DatingForm.

Add a Tab Control

From the Containers Toolbox menu, select a TabControl and place it on the form. Resize it so that it takes up most of the form.

Change the headings. Click TabPages in the properties window; a small box with three dots appears; click this to display the TabPage collection editor. Here you can select the tab pages and change their Text and the TabPage name. Change their Text properties to Name and Address and add the third and call it WLTM details, see figure 2.9. Close the collection editor.

Figure 2.9 The TabControl

Add the details

Select the Name tab and add three labels and change their Text properties to suit (First Name, Last Name and Age). Add two textboxes for the name. Add a NumericUpDown control and change the minimum property to 18. The first tab should be similar to figure 2.10:

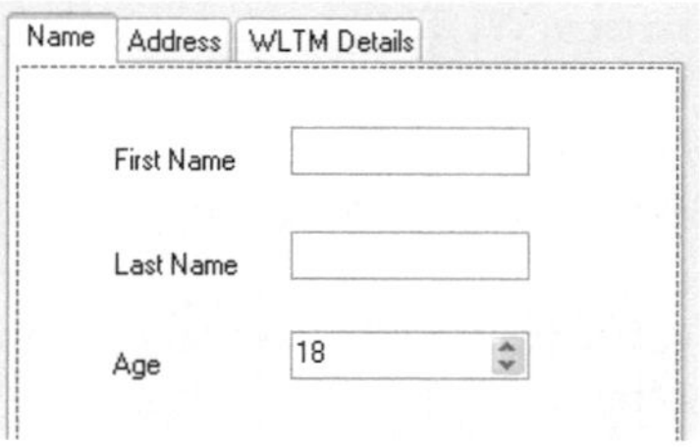

Figure 2.10 Dating Form design - Name

Select the Address tab and add labels and text boxes for the address. Add a list box and add the countries mentioned above using Items collection properties. The design should be similar to figure 2.11:

Figure 2.11 Dating Form design - Address

Finally select the WLTM Details tab and add a GroupBox container to the form change its Text to Interest. Add four CheckBoxes to the GroupBox and change their Text to those mentioned above (or make up your own interests). Note that as they are all grouped together, you can move them around the form as a group.

The WLTM design should be similar to figure 2.12:

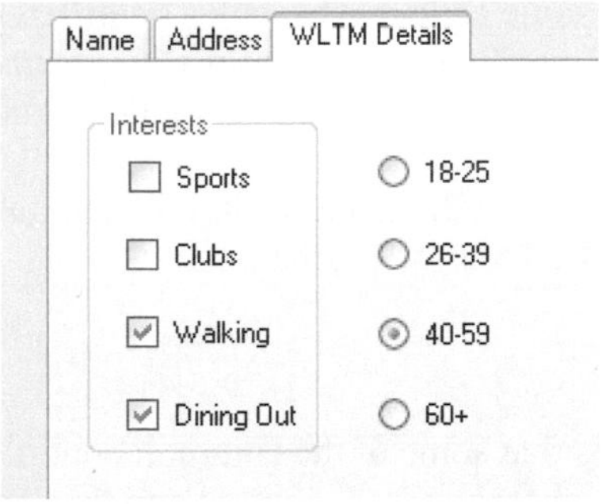

Figure 2.12 Dating Form design – WLTM

Save the project and run the program.

Self Assessment Exercises

1) Watch the third video 'Writing Code to Handle Events and Set Properties' pointed to by Elektor's web site.

2) Experiment with the controls mentioned in section 2.10. Place them on a form and change their properties. If they have a collection of items (e.g. the combo box), add some items to the list and observe its operation.

3) The Tooltip control. The tooltip control provides a hint for your controls. Add a button and a toolTip control to the form (it will display in the status bar). A property 'Tooltip on Tooltip1' is now added to the button. Type a message for this property (e.g. 'Press me'), run the program and hold the mouse cursor over the button. Watch the message appear then disappear.

4) Keyboard entry. Add a textbox to a form. For its KeyDown event, add the following code:

```
if (e.KeyCode == Keys.Enter)
{
        MessageBox.Show("You pressed enter");
        textBox1.Clear();
}
```

5) Note that all the available key identifiers are displayed by the IntelliSense. See if you can find out what the EXSEL key is! Keyboard events and key identifiers are on the www.w3c.org web site.

6) Find a list of the escape (backslash) characters such as \r and \n and what they do.

7) Events. Try writing some code that executes on different events. For example try writing code for a MouseEnter and MouseLeave events for a control. They could be simple MessageBox.Show messages – 'Entered' and 'Left'

8) Find out how to use some other controls in the other tabs, such as the ToolStrip and StatusStrip in the Menus & Toolbars tab.

Summary

In this chapter we have looked at some of the common controls in more detail, including the button, textbox, listbox, checkbox, radio button and their main properties and events. We have seen some of the other events such as Mouse and Keyboard events. Properties, events and methods are the basis of object oriented programming, which is covered later. We have seen that the controls can be grouped together using containers and used these in a design exercise.

3   Dialogs and forms

3.1   Introduction

In the first chapters we saw that controls such as buttons, labels and text boxes, are selected from the toolbox and placed on the form to design the user interface. We also saw that these controls had properties (e.g. height, position on the form), events (e.g. button click) and methods (e.g Add, Insert, Remove). Now we will look at displaying messages and inputting values using dialogs and forms.

3.2   User messages – The Message Box Dialog

You can easily display messages to your users. You will have seen messages boxes and prompts in other windows applications. We shall see how to add them in our code.

Dialogs are used to display information. They are not controls you place on your form but appear when the program runs. You can use standard dialogs or create your own using forms.

The simplest way to display a message is to use a MessageBox, see figure 3.1. The code is simply **MessageBox.Show** followed by the string to be displayed, e.g:

MessageBox.Show("Displayed using MessageBox.Show( );");

Figure 3.1 ShowMessage procedure display

To try this, place a button on a form and insert the above code for the button click event.

Note there is no caption. You can display a caption by passing a second string to the MessageBox.Show() method, i.e.:

MessageBox.Show("text","caption");

You may want to have more than just the OK button displayed and you can extend the **Show( )** method further to add common buttons such as Yes/No/Cancel, OK/Cancel, Abort/Retry/Ignore. You can also add an icon such as an exclamation from a selection of icons. To do this you add the message buttons and icon after the text and caption, for example:

```
MessageBox.Show("This will format your disk!", "Format caption",
        MessageBoxButtons.OKCancel, MessageBoxIcon.Exclamation);
```

Figure 3.2 shows how it is displayed.

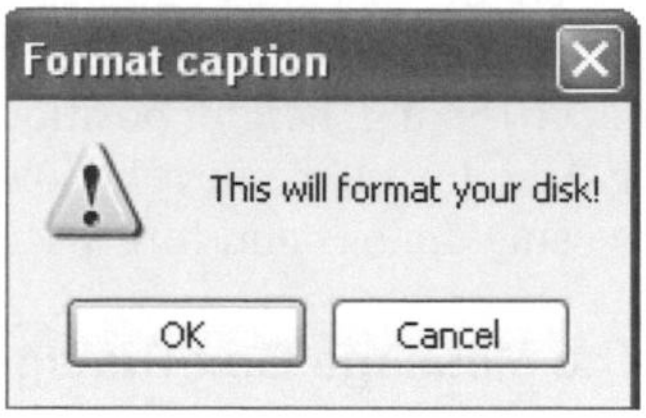

Figure 3.2 MessageBox with response buttons

You can find out the button groups and icons by letting the C# IntelliSense prompt you with the options.

As we have seen before, numbers are converted to strings automatically, you can type:

```
MessageBox.Show("You are "+25);
```

And to display multiple lines use \r and \n (return and new line), for example:

```
MessageBox.Show("You are \r\n"+25);
```

You have no control over where the message box is placed. We shall see how we can design our own message box (using a new form) to do this later.

3.2.1 Message Reply

Of course we want to know which button is selected and we have to write code to deal with the button press.

The Show method returns a response value (a DialogResult) which indicates which button was pressed. This can then be used to determine the program's operation.

Exercise: Dealing with responses

Enter this code for a ButtonClick procedure and see what happens:

```
if (MessageBox.Show("This will format your disk!", "Formatting disk",
    MessageBoxButtons.OKCancel, MessageBoxIcon.Exclamation) ==
        DialogResult.OK)
  {
    MessageBox.Show("Formatting disk");
  }
```

```
        else
        {
          MessageBox.Show("Did not format disk");
        }
```

Here the reply is compared (using the '= =' operation) and if the OK button is pressed the Dialog result is DialogResult.OK and formatting would take place otherwise (else) it does not format the disk.

Note what we have been doing with the simple MessageBox.Show( ) method. Initially we used it to display a message, but then the same method was extended to add a caption, buttons and icons. This is one of the features of object oriented programming. The IntelliSense knows all the possible Show method calls and lists them as you type.

3.3   Creating your own dialogs - Prompting for input

The MessageBox.Show( ) is very versatile, but there is no method to prompt for input from the user. To do this you have to create your own message box using forms. We shall do this as an exercise.

3.3.1   User input - Adding forms exercise

Start a new Windows application project and save it, calling it 'Forms'. Add a button to form1. Rename the button btnShowForm and give it a caption 'Show my dialog'.

Now we are going to create our custom dialog form. Add a new form to the project using Project> Add Windows Form, and select Windows form. The new form appears. You might like to take this opportunity of seeing what else you can add, for example the standard Help> About form can be added. For now use the default name of the form, form2, see figure 3.3

Figure 3.3. Adding a new form

Change the Text property of the new form to 'Custom dialog box'.
Add a text box to the new form and change its properties as follows:

Name:	txtCustomMessage – let's give it a sensible name,
MultiLine:	True – let's allow many lines of text. Doing this gives you sizing handles, so make it almost fill the form.

Add some lines of text. Click the Text property and add the first line, click the down arrow and add more lines of text.

Finally add buttons for the response. Add one with the text 'Cancel', and one with the text 'OK'. We want them to provide a response, so change their DialogResult property to 'Cancel' and 'OK' respectively. Select these from the drop down box in the DialogResult property, see figure 3.4.

Figure 3.4 Dialog Result options

Your design should be similar to Figure 3.5.

Figure3.5 Custom Dialog Box

In this case we want to ensure the user clicks one of the buttons before continuing, and not ignore this prompt. Hence to show the form we will use the method **ShowDialog( )**. This is known as a modal form. If you want to show a form that can be ignored by the user just use the method **Show( )**;

Note that you don't have to write code to close the form, clicking the button will close it automatically.

Now we need to write the code to display our dialog box. Display form1 (double-click form1.cs in the solution explorer if it isn't displayed) and double-click the 'Show my dialog' button you added. Add the following code for the button click:

```
private void btnShowForm_Click(object sender, EventArgs e)
{
   Form2 dialogForm = new Form2( );
   if (dialogForm.ShowDialog( ) == DialogResult.OK)
   {
      MessageBox.Show("You clicked OK");
   }
   else
   {
      MessageBox.Show("You clicked Cancel");
   } // end if .. else
} // end button Click
```

Note how we create and use Form2, we declare it in the first line and give it a name new name dialogForm. We use this name later in the code.

Run the program. Clicking the button should display form2. You can then click OK or Cancel.

We have managed to show a second form, but haven't yet passed value between the forms. Before we do that, let's look at the timer component and 'splash' forms.

3.4   Splash forms and the Timer control

Now we know how to display a second form, we can display a 'splash' form that will show for a short time before the main application starts. It will close itself. We will use the timer control to do this.

Exercise: A splash form

Create a new application, call it Splash and create a directory for the solution. Select the form and in the Properties box, display the events ⚡ for the form in the Properties box. Scroll to the Activated event and click this to display the code for the Form1_Activated event. Add the following code for the event:

```
Form2 frm2Show = new Form2( );    // create a new form
frm2Show.Show( );                 // and show it
```

When form1 is loaded it will show Form2. Remember, we could have used ShowDilaog to display a modal form that cannot be ignored, i.e. a password dialog.

Now add a second form (Project > Add Windows Form > Windows form). Use the default name (form2). Add a label to form2 changing its caption to 'Hello'. Add a timer control from the toolbox component tab to form2:

This is a non-visual component (it's not seen at run-time) and will be displayed in the status bar. The timer code will run every interval if the timer is enabled. Its most used properties are:

Name :	The usual meaning,
Enabled:	True or False,
Interval :	Time in milliseconds - default 100, and
Tag :	free for use by your application.

Change the timer's Enabled property to true and the Interval to 1000.
Double-click the icon and add the following code for the timer tick event:

```
this.Close( );
```

Run the program and observe its operation.

Even though form1 is the main form, it displays form2 when it is loaded. Form2 closes itself on the timer event. You may find that form2 is displayed behind form1. In this case, change form2's TopMost property to true and run the program again.

Look again at the timer code: this.Close( ); Remember the keyword 'this' refers to the current object, in this case the form with the timer code.

3.5   Accessing controls on other forms

Now that we know how to create and display a second form, let's see how to access controls on the second form.

Remember when we add a form to our project, that's all we do. To display it we have to create an instance of it and show it. Any controls on a form are private to that form, so to access them from another form we either have to declare them public or preferably, call a public method (you may know this as a procedure or subroutine) which accesses the object.

Let's suppose we have a form1 with a button, which we want to change the text in a textbox on form2.

The code for the button on Form1 is:

```
Form2 f2 = new Form2( );
f2.setTextBox1("Hello");          // call the setTextBox method in form2
                                  // to change the text
f2.Show( );                       // and show the form
```

Now create a public method on form2 which is called to change the (private to form1) textbox:

```
public void setTextBox1(string temp)
{
    this.textBox1.Text = temp;
}
```

To access a control, say a textbox (textBox1), on form1 from the second form, add a method to access the text on textbox as follows:

```
public void SetTextBox(string strText)
{
    textBox1.Text = strText;
}
```

To show form2 (when we've created it), add the following to Form1_Load:

```
private void Form1_Load(object sender, EventArgs e)
{
    new Form2(this).Show();
}
```

Now add the second form – Form2. Change code at the top to:

```
public partial class Form2 : Form
{
    Form1 parent;
    public Form2(Form1 p)
    {
        InitializeComponent();
        parent = p;
    }
```

Add button and for the button click code, add:

```
private void button1_Click(object sender, EventArgs e)
{
    parent.SetTextBox("hello there");
}
```

Click the button and form1's textbox should change.

Self Assessment Exercises

1. Snap game using Timers and the Random object

This exercise randomly displays different colours in a picture box and displays a message if the colours are the same. It uses timers and picture boxes and introduces random numbers.

- Place a Timer from the component palette on the form. This will not show at run-time. When the timer code runs it will check for a snap and generate new colours. Make sure its properties are: Enabled = True and Interval = 500 (1/2 second).

- Add two Pictureboxes to the form. Change their BackColor property to Web>Red. Our program will change their colour and display a Message box if they compare.

Find the C# code:
```
public partial class Form1 : Form
```

After the open curly bracket { and before the code: 'public Form1( )', add the following to declare a Random object and an integer identifier to hold the number:

```
Random randomColour = new Random( );      // declare a random object
int randomNumber;                         // integer to hold a random number
```

Double-click the timer component and enter the following code between the curly brackets:

```
if (pictureBox1.BackColor == pictureBox2.BackColor)
{
    timer1.Enabled = false;          // if colours are the same stop the timer
    MessageBox.Show("Snap!");        // and display message
    timer1.Enabled = true;           // start timer when message is OKed
}

// Generate new colours
randomNumber = randomColour.Next(3);        // random number 0 to 2
// change pictureBox1 colour
if (randomNumber == 0) pictureBox1.BackColor = Color.Blue;
if (randomNumber == 1) pictureBox1.BackColor = Color.Green;
if (randomNumber == 2) pictureBox1.BackColor = Color.Red;

randomNumber = randomColour.Next(3);        // random number 0 to 2
// change pictureBox2 colour
```

```
if (randomNumber == 0) pictureBox2.BackColor = Color.Blue;
if (randomNumber == 1) pictureBox2.BackColor = Color.Green;
if (randomNumber == 2) pictureBox2.BackColor = Color.Red;
```

Run the program and see how it works. We will look at the 'if' statement soon.

Random

The random object has to be instantiated (e.g. `Random rndObj = new Random( );` - we'll explain this later) and a random number generated using '.Next', e.g.
`randomNumber = rndObj.Next();`

'Next' has three possibilities:

1) `randomObj.Next( );`
   > returns a non-negative random number:
   > `int intRandom = rndObj.Next();`

2) `randomObj.Next(int maxValue);`
   > returns a value from 0 to maxValue-1.
   > `int intRandom = rndObj.Next(5);   // random number 0 - 4`

3) `randomObj.Next(int minValue, int maxValue);`
   > returns a value between minValue and maxValue-1.
   > `int intRandom = rndObj.Next(3,7);         // number from 3 to 6`

You can obtain a floating point random number using `rndObj.NextDouble()` which returns a value equal or greater than 0.0 but less than 1, as follows:

```
double randomDouble = rndObj.NextDouble();                  // gives 0 - 0.99999
// or
double randomDouble = 15 + 10*rndObj.NextDouble();          // gives 15 - 24.999
```

2. Extend the program to

1) Add a second timer with a different Interval to control the second picture box.

2) Add a button and a text box for the user to play Snap. The user is to click the button when (s)he sees a snap. The text box will contain the score.
   Increment a counter if the player guesses correctly, and decrement it if it is incorrect or a Snap is missed. The counter could be a value in a text box; you will have to convert its text from a string to an integer to increment the number.

3) Add a stop/stop button to control the program. If its caption is 'Start', change it from 'Start' to 'Stop and enable the timer, otherwise (else) change its caption

(from Stop) to Start and disable the timer. You will have to use an 'if .. then .. else' statement:

```
if (StartStopButton.Text == "Start")
   {
   // change caption to Stop and enable timer
   }
else
   {
   // change caption to Start and disable timer
   }
```

4) Fully debug and test the program. E.g. can the user guess more than once for a match?

Summary

This chapter has covered using the MessageBox dialog to display simple messages and dealing with the button click response. This was extended to design and display our own forms. This was taken further to design a splash form which introduced the non-visual timer control. We have also covered how to access objects on one form from another.

In the self assessment exercises, by designing a snap game, the random object was introduced.

4 The C# Language – the basics

4.1 Introduction

As well as designing our user interface we have to write some code. We will start by looking at the basic data types, assignments and comparisons. In the next chapter we will look at decision making with control and program flow.

4.2 Declarations - Variables and Data type identifiers.

All variables must have a data type and a name or identifier. Before we can use a variable or constant its data type (e.g. integer, floating point, string) and its name must be declared. This can be done at any time before (or when) the variable is used.

A variable is declared by stating its data type followed by its name. It can optionally be given an initial value. We saw the following declaration in Chapter 2. It :

```
string strMessage = "Cancel";
```

This declares a string data type called strMessage with the initial value "Cancel".

Constants are defined by adding the reserved word const, for example:

```
const float GOLDENRATIO = 1.61803399F;
```

You must declare an initial value for a constant.

C# supports nine integral data types, two floating point types, a type suitable for financial calculations, types for characters and strings and a type for Boolean logical variables (true and false). The data types and example declarations are shown in table 4.1.

Data type	Example declaration	Description
byte	byte eightBits = 128;	0 to 255
sbyte	sbyte signedByte = -128;	-128 to +127
short	short signedWord = 32767;	-32768 to 32767
int	int bigNumber = 1234567;	-2147483648 to +2147483647
long	long evenBigger = 12345678;	Large integer
float	float fltNumber = 0.23F;	Approx. -3.4E38 to +3.4E38
double	double dblFloatingPoint = 2.345D;	Approx -1.79E208 to +1.79E208
decimal	decimal decMoney = 3.33M;	Used for currency
bool	bool bolTrueFalse = true;	TRUE or FALSE
char	char chrA = 'A';	Letters of the alphabet : 'A' or '*'
string	string strAString = "this is a string";	Approx 0 to 2 billion chars
uint	uint uintLarge = 543210;	Unsigned, 0 to 4,294,967,295
ushort	ushort ushtMedium = 43210;	Unsigned, 0 to 65535
ulong	ulong ulngLong = 0;	Unsigned, 0 to 10^{20}

Table 4.1 C# data types

4.2.1 Naming convention

As we have said it is a good idea to adopt a convention when naming your variables, constants and (when we come to them) methods and class names so that by just looking at the name you know what they are. I have already suggested you use three letters to indicate the type of control placed on a form, e.g. btn, lbl, txt etc. It's common to use all capital letters for constants.

You can of course use your own rules, but by convention variables start with a lowercase letter separating each word with a capital letter. e.g. loopCount, moneyOwed and classes will begin with a capital letter, e.g. CalculateSine, SquareNumber.

Preferred naming conventions can be found by searching for 'C# naming convention' on the MSDN site at http://msdn.microsoft.com

4.2.2 Some declaration examples:

Here are some examples of declaring variables and constants:

```
        const double MYCONSTANT =2.14159;
        const int MAXSIZE = 10, MINSIZE = 1;   // more than one in a line
        const ushort HEXNUMBER = 0xCAFE;   // 0x used for hexadecimal

        int integerNumber;                     // not initialised
        double temperature = 98.6;
        char letterA, letterB;
        bool lightSwitch = true;
```

4.3   Assignments and operators

Assignments are made with the equals symbols '=' and end with a semicolon, for example

Example: sum = one + two;

The usual operators are used: add +, subtract -, multiply *, divide / and remainder %, as is the order of their operation (precedence): Unary (e.g. 'not'), brackets, division and multiplication, add and subtract.

4.3.1   Shortcuts

Variables can be incremented and decremented using the shortcuts '++' and '--'. These operators can be put both before and after the variable to be changed. You can have x++ or ++x. In most cases it doesn't make any difference, but if you are assigning the value to another variable it will. For instance the following code displays the value 0.

```
int x;
int y = 0;
x = y++;                        // assign to x then increment y
MessageBox.Show(x.ToString());
```

Whereas this code displays the value 1:

```
int x;
int y = 0;
x = ++y;                        // increment y, then assign y to x
MessageBox.Show(x.ToString());
```

In both cases, y ends up with the value 1.

Assignments such as x=x+y; can be shortened as well. In this case to x+=y;
Note that it's not shortened to x=+y;. This is useful for objects with long names.

The shortened versions are:

add = add + 3;	becomes	add += 3;
div = div / 4;	becomes	div /= 4;
mult = mult * 5;	becomes	mult *= 5;
sub = sub - 2;	becomes	sub -= 2;
remainder = remainder%4;	becomes	remainder %= 4;

4.4   Comments

```
/*
Slash-star is a multi-line comment- it is ended with a star-slash
*/
// or you can use a double slash which ignores the rest of the line
```

You can comment (or uncomment) sections of selected code using the icons:

4.5   Casting (converting) data types

You may find that you have to convert from one data type to another to perform an operation. We have already seen conversions from numbers to strings. Conversions can be implicit or explicit.

Implicit conversions are done automatically and guarantee that no data is lost in the conversion. For instance you can convert a single precision 'float' data type to 'double' without a problem because the double encompasses the float. However if you try to convert a double precision variable to single precision some data may be lost and you have to explicitly say that it's OK. Consider the following code:

```
double dbli=1.234;    // declare a double precision number
float fltj=1.234F;    // declaration a single precision floating-point number
dbli = fltj;          // is OK you can convert float to double
fltj = dbli;          // this errors – it requires an explicit cast
```

The 'double' data type has more precision than 'float', so the line of code 'fltj = dbl;'errors, requesting an explicit cast. If you only require a result to single precision, then you can explicitly say the change is OK but placing **(float)** in front of 'dbli', as follows:

```
fltj = (float) dbli;    // the (float) indicates that you say it's OK
```

Table 4.2 shows a list of safe conversions:

Data type	Can be converted to
byte	char, short, int, long, float, double, decimal
short	int, long, float, double, decimal
int	long, float, double, decimal
long	float, double, decimal
float	double, decimal
double	decimal

Table 4.2 Safe data type conversions

Integer divides are automatically truncated, e.g:

```
integerNumber = 124 / 3;
MessageBox.Show(integerNumber.ToString( ));        // displays 41
integerNumber = integerNumber % 3;
MessageBox.Show(integerNumber.ToString( ));  // remainder
```

4.6   Characters and strings

Characters are declared by using a single quote around the character and strings defined using double quotes. As we have seen, strings that represent a number (e.g. a number typed into a text box) can be converted using the Parse method such as float.Parse(string) or int.Parse(string). Examples are:

```
char chrCapitalA = 'A';
string strAString = "this is a string";
string strOneChar = "a";          // a one character string!
string strNumber = "1.234";
float fltNumber =  float.Parse(strNumber);
int integerNumber = int.Parse("123");
int intNumber = (int)Math.Round(float.Parse(strNumber));
```

4.7   Logical operations – Boolean data type

The Boolean data type (bool) can be used in cases where only true or false conditions exist. Logic operations can be performed on Boolean and other data types. The logic operations are 'NOT', 'AND', 'OR' and 'XOR' - exclusive or, and are performed with the symbols: !, &, |, and ^. The logic operations are shown in Table 4.3.

A	B	!A	A & B	A | B	A ^ B
		NOT	AND	OR	EXOR
0	0	1	0	0	0
0	1	1	0	1	1
1	0	0	0	1	1
1	1	0	1	1	0

Table 4.3 Logic Operations

4.8   Mathematical Functions

C# provides a Math class. Some of the more common Math tasks are shown below.

Name	Description
Abs	Returns the absolute value of a number.
Acos, Asin, Atan	Returns the angle in radians for the (sin, cos or tan) of the number.
Sin, Cos, Tan	Returns the sine, cosine, tangent of an angle measured in radians.
Cosh, Sinh, Tanh	Returns the hyperbolic (sine, cosine, tangent) of an angle.
Exp	Returns e raised to the specified power.

IEEERemainder	Returns the remainder from the division of two numbers.
Log	Returns the logarithm of a specified number.
Log10	Returns the base 10 logarithm of a specified number.
Max	Returns the larger of two specified numbers.
Min	Returns the smaller of two numbers.
Pow	Returns a number raised to a specified power.
Round	Rounds a value to the nearest integer or number of decimal places.
Sqrt	Returns the square root of a specified number.
ToString	Returns a String that represents the current Object.
Truncate	Calculates the integral part of a number.

4.9   Date and Time

The DateTime structure is split into a date part and a time part. The date holds a date, month and year, and the time holds hours, minutes, seconds and milliseconds. The smallest interval between two DateTime values is one hundred nanoseconds and is called a tick.

DateTime is a structure, and you have to instantiate it before you can use it as follows:

```
DateTime xmas2007 = new DateTime(2007, 12, 25);
    // will also contain time – Midnight
```

You can also set the hours and minutes using:

```
DateTime newDate = new DateTime(2001, 2, 3, 4, 5, 6, 7);
    // 3 Feb 2001 04:05:06.0007
```

You can find out the current date and time using the property Now and calculate a time span using TimeSpan:

```
// declare Xmas 2007
DateTime xmas2007 = new DateTime(2007, 12, 25);
DateTime theTime = new DateTime( );
theTime = DateTime.Now;                         // get time now
label1.Text = theTime.ToString( );
TimeSpan tspan = theTime - xmas2007;        // difference?
int daysToXmas = tspan.Days;    // also .Hours, .Minutes, .Seconds etc.
label2.Text = "Time since Christmas 2007 = "+  tspan.ToString( );
label3.Text = "Days since Christmas 2007 = " + tspan.Days.ToString( );
```

4.9.1   DateTime properties and methods

You might want to extract the date or time from a DateTime object. Some of the DateTime properties are:

Month	xmas2007.Month	// returns 12
Day	xmas2007.Day	// returns 25
DayOfWeek	xmas2007.DayOfWeek	// returns DayOfWeek.Tuesday

The DateTime class also contains methods such as:

Add	adds a timespan	
AddDays	Adds a number of days	xmas2007.AddDays(7); // new year
AddYears	Adds a number of years	xmas2007.AddYears(1); // xmas2008

There are also AddMilliseconds, AddSeconds, AddMonths and others.

4.10 Scope

The scope of an identifier (such as a variable or method) refers to the region of code where it exists and can be accessed. The scope can be block or class scope. Generally, classes have public scope and methods and variables have private scope. The public and private keywords allow you to override these defaults. They can only be used at the class level, not within a method.

4.10.1 Block scope

When an identifier is declared within a block of code or method, i.e. within curly brackets, it is given block scope. It is then accessible within the block but not outside it. For instance:

```
if (true)
{
  int blockVariable=0;            // blockVariable only exists here.
}
// blockVariable not accessible here
```

The block can be a block within curly brackets as above or a method such as a button click.

4.10.2 Class scope

The class code starts after the open curly bracket after the class statement, e.g.:

```
public class Form1 : Form
 {
        // class code and scope starts here.
```

Identifiers declared at this level are accessible by all the code within the class.

The following code may help explain the scope of some variables.

```
public class Form1 : Form
// class Form1 is public and accessible to other classes.

{
    int ClassVariable;        // accessible within this class
    private void button1_Click(object sender, EventArgs e)
    {
        int MethodVariable1;         // accessible only in this button click
        ClassVariable = 3;           // is OK
        {                            // new block of code
            int BlockVariable;       // only exists in this block
            MethodVariable1 = 0;     // is OK
            BlockVariable = 1;       // is OK
        }
        BlockVariable = 2;           // is an error
    }

    private void button2_Click(object sender, EventArgs e)
    {
        int MethodVariable2;         // accessible only in this method
        ClassVariable = 4;           // is OK
        MethodVariable2 = 1;         // is OK
        MethodVariable1 = 5;         // is an error
    }
}
```

You should use private scope where possible, otherwise it makes programs more difficult to understand and debug.

We shall see more on scope when we look at the chapters on methods and objects.

For more examples on scope see the self assessment exercises.

Self Assessment Exercises

1. Watch the 'Working with Variables, Expressions, Statements and Operators in C#' video pointed to by Elektor's web site.

2. Variables
Declare variables with different data types. Try to assign them to each other and see the error messages. Where possible try to cast from one data type to another.

Declare some variables in one button click code and see if they can be accessed by separate button click code.

3. Scope.

Place two buttons on a form and change their button click code as follows. Note the regions of code where the string variables exist.

```
public partial class Form1 : Form
{
    string strClassString = "ClassString";

    private void button1_Click(object sender, EventArgs e)
    {
        string strMethodString = "MethodString";
        MessageBox.Show(strMyClassString);    // is OK
        MessageBox.Show(strMethodString);     // is OK
    }

    private void button2_Click(object sender, EventArgs e)
    {
        MessageBox.Show(strClassString);    // is OK
        MessageBox.Show(strMethodString);  // will error

    }
```

Find out in which regions of code you can declare the strings as public or private.

Declare a second strClassString on the first line of the button2_Click code as follows, and see what happens.

```
string strClassString = "newString";
```

This is a different strClassString from the first one declared.

4. DateTime exercise. Write a program that works out how many days there are until your birthday.

Summary

This chapter has covered the basic C# language constructs of data types, assignment and casting or converting data types. Characters and strings have been seen as well as mathematical and logic operations. Further concepts, such as scope and more detailed data types such as DateTime have also been covered.

5   The C# Language – arrays, structures and strings

5.1   Introduction

In this chapter we will cover arrays and strings. Arrays enable us to hold many items of the same data type. Strings are arrays of characters. We shall see how to declare arrays and strings and see some of the methods associated with them. We shall also see how to declare and use variable size, or dynamic, arrays.

5.2   Arrays

Arrays are used to hold a number of items of the same type of data, e.g. a list of peoples' ages, birth dates or salary. You declare an array before using it using square brackets '[ ]' and then set its size, as follows:

```
int[ ] intArray;              // an integer array called intArray.
intArray = new int[20];       // create array with 20 items – from 0 to 19
```

You can also declare and fill the array with data in one line of code as follows:

```
int[ ] myArray = { 1, 2, 3, 4, 5 };
// or
string[ ] arrayOfNames = { "Peter", "Paul", "Mary" };
```

Individual items in an array are accessed using a number in the square brackets. The item within the square brackets is known as the index and can be an expression. The index starts at zero; the last index is the size of the array minus 1. Using the array declared above, for example:

```
intArray[0] = 5;                  // sets the first element to 5
intArray[1] = intArray[6*3+1];    // copy the last element [19]
                                  // to the second element
```

If your program accesses an index outside the size of the array, then a run-time error message will occur. If you don't know how large your array needs to be, you can either create one that you know will be large enough or use a dynamic array type which automatically changes its size to suit. We shall see how to do this later.

Arrays have properties, the most useful of which is 'Length' which, as it suggests, provides the length of the array. Hence the last item's index is always Length-1. For example:

```
intArray[intArray.Length-1] = 25;      // set the last element
```

Arrays also have methods such as CopyTo( ).

5.3   Multidimensional arrays

Multidimensional arrays, i.e. ones with more than one index can be also be defined. For example a two dimensional array of students' scores would be defined by:

```
int [ , ] score;              // declare 2D array of integer data type
score = new int[3,2];         // set size 3 rows by 2 columns
```

This creates an array of three indexes (three students) each with two items, as follows:

	Exam 1	Exam 2
Student 1	score[0,0]	score[0,1]
Student 2	score[1,0]	score[1,1]
Student 3	score[2,0]	score[2,1]

To set the array values use the code:

```
score[0,1] = 68;      // Set exam 2 mark of student 1.
```

Two dimensional arrays can also be defined and initialised in one go, as follows:

```
double [ , ] twoDArray = { { 0.1, 1.1 }, { 2.1, 3.1 }, { 4.1, 5 } };
// is the same as
double [ , ] twoDArray = new double[3, 2]
        {{ 0.1, 1.1 }, { 2.1, 3.1 }, { 4.1, 5 }} ;
```

This can be extended to three and more dimensions as follows:

```
int[ , , ] my3Darray;
my3Darray = new int[2, 3, 4];
my3Darray[1, 2, 3] = 2;

int[ , , , ] my4Darray;
my4Darray = new int[2, 3, 4, 5];
my4Darray[1, 2, 3, 4] = 6;
```

You can also define multidimensional arrays with irregular sizes. These are known as jagged arrays. The following code shows how an array with 2, 4 and 6 elements may be created:

```
int[ ][ ] jagArray = new int[3][ ];    // create multidimensional array
jagArray [0] = new int [2];
jagArray [1] = new int [4];
jagArray [2] = new int [6];
jagArray[0][1] = 9;                    // last in array [0]
jagArray[1][3] = 10;                   // last in array [1]
```

```
jagArray[2][5] = 11;                          // last in array [2]
```

Each jagArray[ ] holds a reference to a single-dimensional integer array.

5.3   Structures

You might want to create a simple array containing different data types. For instance, you might want a list of employees which contains their name, age and gender, salary etc. This is a structure, but is also sometimes called a record.

The individual data types in the structure are to be declared along with a way of accessing and changing the values. We will see this in more detail when we cover classes, but for now let's look at an example.

A structure is defined using the keyword 'struct'. The data types are declared followed by a way of accessing them. The keyword 'this' is used to access the data. You can create as many versions of the structure as you want and 'this' refers to the contents of an individual version instantiated. An example personnel record structure might be as follows:

```
struct personnelRecord
{                              // declare the data types
    public string name;
    public int age;
    public double salary;
    public char gender;

// Access to the data. Note the same name (personnelRecord) is used

    public personnelRecord(string name, int age,
                           double salary, char gender)
    {
        this.name = name;
        this.age = age;
        this.salary = salary;
        this.gender = gender;
    }
} // end declaration of struct
```

This has only declared the structure it still needs to be instantiated with the 'new' keyword, as we did with arrays. The structure must be declared at the top of the class, e.g. after the line of code: public class Form1 : Form {

A personnel list array of type personnelRecord is instantiated and its elements accessed as follows:

60

```
// one structure:
personnelRecord  myEmployees = new personnelRecord( );
myEmployees.age = 21;
myEmployees.gender = 'M';

// array of 10:
personnelRecord[ ] personnelList = new personnelRecord[10];
personnelList[0].name = "John Allwork";
personnelList[9].salary = 9999.99;
```

Note we use the dot notation to access the data just as we did with properties for our controls.

You might want to have some actions for your personnel such as change name, promote or increase salary – these would be its methods. This leads us to classes and object oriented programming, which we will cover later.

5.3.1   The public declaration

We covered the public keyword briefly in the previous chapter. In the above code we have declared the individual variables in the structure as 'public'. If we had not done this, the items would only exist within the structure's block of code (within the curly brackets). Obviously we want to use these items outside the structure and declaring them as public allows this to happen. We will cover this in more detail in the chapter on objects.

See the self assessment exercises for more on structures.

5.4   Character arrays and strings

Characters are variables of type char that hold a keyboard character (e.g. letters, numbers and symbols). Characters are held in UTF-8 format, which enables any language character to be used and is backward compatible with ASCII. Strings are a special type of array that holds characters.

As we have seen the data held in a text box is a string and individual characters from a text box can be treated as an array element as follows:

```
char chrText;                        // declare char
chrText = textBox1.Text[2];          // read 3rd character from textbox
textBox1.Text = chrText.ToString( ); // convert char to string
                                     // and display in textbox
```

Note the conversion from the char to the string to allow us to write back to the text box.

You can declare an array of chars as follows:

```
char[ ] charArray;
charArray = new chr[20];    // 20 elements in the array - index 0 to 19
```

5.5   String manipulation

C# .NET provides a number of methods to manipulate strings such as compare, split, search, change case etc.

We have already seen how we can concatenate strings (add one string onto the end of another) using the + operator, e.g.:

```
MessageBox.Show("This string has" + " this string added to it");
```

Of course the strings could have been previously declared and used as follows:

```
string string1 = "This string has";
string string2 = " this string added to it";
MessageBox.Show(string1 + string2);
```

We can determine the length of a string with the length property:

```
int intLength;
string strOfChars = "This string has 29 characters";
intLength = strOfChars.Length;
MessageBox.Show(intLength.ToString( ));       // will display 29
```

Or we could have had:

```
MessageBox.Show((("This string has 29 characters").Length).ToString( ));
```

5.6   String conversion

Just to remind you how to convert between strings and numbers, you can convert from integers or floating point numbers to strings using the .ToString method:

```
int i = 10;
float f = 123456.22f;
double d = 123.567;
MessageBox.Show("int= " +i.ToString( )+"float= " +
        f.ToString( )+"double= "+d.ToString( ));
```

To convert from a string to a number, use the Parse method. There are many Parse methods. int.Parse and Int32.Parse converts from a string to an integer and float.Parse and double.Parse convert from a string to a floating point number, etc. For example:

```
string strFpNo = "123456.22";
string strIntNo = "12345";
MessageBox.Show("decimal= " + decimal.Parse(strFpNo));
MessageBox.Show("float= " + float.Parse(strFpNo));
MessageBox.Show("integer= " + int.Parse(strIntNo));
```

5.7   String methods

5.7.1   The Substring( ) method.

Part of a string can be retrieved using the Substring( ) method. The start position and
number of characters is passed to the method and it returns the string. The first character
is 0. For example:

```
MessageBox.Show(("Mary had a little lamb").Substring(2,5));
        // displays 'ry ha'
MessageBox.Show(("Mary had a little lamb").Substring(0,4));
        // displays 'Mary'
```

5.7.2   The IndexOf( ) and IndexOfAny( ) methods.

You can determine if one string is contained within another using the IndexOf( ) method.
The string you wish to find is passed to the method and it returns the index of the string
or -1 if it isn't found. This method is case sensitive. For example:

```
MessageBox.Show(("Mary had a little lamb").IndexOf("ry ha").ToString( ));
// displays 2
MessageBox.Show(("Mary had a little lamb").IndexOf("mar").ToString( ));
// displays -1
```

This method can also be called with an integer starting index and a number of characters
to search. For example:

- IndexOf(searchString);
- IndexOf(searchString, startIndex);
- IndexOf(searchString, startIndex, numberOfCharsToSearch);

Some examples are:

```
MessageBox.Show(("Mary had a lamb").IndexOf("ry ha",1).ToString( ));
// finds 'ry ha' at second index and displays 2

MessageBox.Show(("Mary had a lamb").IndexOf("ry ha",6).ToString( ));
// starts searching at position 6, doesn't find 'ry ha', and displays -1

MessageBox.Show(("Mary had a lamb").IndexOf("ry ha",1,2).ToString( ));
```

```
// starts at postion 1, looks for 2 characters,
// doesn't find 'ry ha' and displays -1

MessageBox.Show(("Mary had a lamb").IndexOf("ry ha",1,6).ToString( ));
// starts at postion 1, looks for 6 characters, finds 'ry ha' and displays 2
```

The IndexOfAny( ) method returns the first occurrence of any letters specified in a char array. For example:

```
string letters = "abcedfghijkl";
char[ ] searchLetters = { 'c', 'A', '$' };
letters.IndexOfAny(searchLetters);              // finds 'c' at index 2.
```

The methods LastIndexOf( ) and LastIndexOfAny( ) perform the same operations but start at the end of the string.

5.7.3   Dealing with spaces – the Trim and Remove methods

The IndexOf( ) method could be used to find spaces, but the following methods are available to deal with spaces:

Trim( )	Removes spaces from the beginning and end of a string.
TrimEnd( )	Removes spaces from the end of a string.
TrimStart( )	Removes spaces from the beginning of a string.
Remove( )	Removes a specified number of spaces from a position in a string

5.7.4   The Replace method

Strings can easily be replaced using the Replace( ) method. The text to be replaced and the replacing text are both passed to the method. The string is searched and the text replaced. For example:

```
string strMaryText = "Mary had a little lamb";
MessageBox.Show(strMaryText);
string strReplacedText = strMaryText.Replace("little lamb", "black sheep");
MessageBox.Show(strReplacedText);
```

Note that all occurrences are replaced, so the following code replaces every letter 'a' with the letter 'i':

```
string strMaryText = "Mary had a little lamb";
MessageBox.Show(strMaryText);
string strReplacedText = strMaryText.Replace("a", "i");
MessageBox.Show(strReplacedText);
// displays Miry hid i little limb
```

5.7.5   The Split method - parsing strings

Strings can be parsed and individual words extracted from the strings by delimiters using the Split( ) method. This method takes an array of chars containing the chars to be used as delimiters, e.g. spaces, commas colons etc. and the individual words can be extracted.

The following code uses the delimiter characters space, comma, full stop, colon and tab to extract the individual words from the string: 'Delimiters are:colon\ttab space,comma.fullStop end'

It displays the original text and finds 8 words as shown in figures 5.1 and 5.2. It then displays them individually.

```
char[ ] delimiterChars = { ' ',   ',',   '.',   ':',   '\t' };
//delimiter characters are: space,comma,full stop,colon and tab

string text = "Delimiters are:colon\ttab space,comma.fullStop end";
MessageBox.Show("Original text: "+ text);

string[ ] words = text.Split(delimiterChars);
MessageBox.Show("Number of words in text:"+ words.Length);

foreach (string s in words)              // we'll see the foreach statement later
{
    MessageBox.Show(s);
}
```

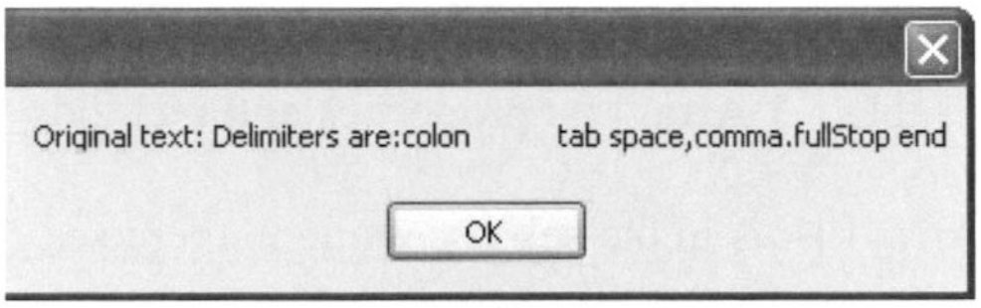

Figure 5.1 Delimiter text

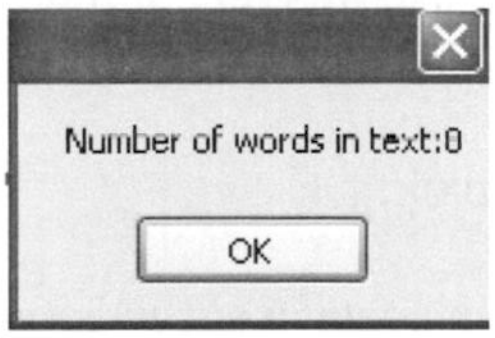

Figure 5.2 Number of words found

5.7.6   Upper and lower case methods

The ToUpper( ) and ToLower( ) methods convert a string to upper case and to lower case respectively.

5.8   Dynamic Arrays. The ArrayList Class

Dynamic arrays are ones which change their size as required as the program runs. They are implemented using an ArrayList. The array list is found in the Collections namespace (or library) and an ArrayList called arrayOfItems is declared as follows:

```
System.Collections.ArrayList arrayOfItems =
            new System.Collections.ArrayList( );
```

You do not have to specify a data type for an ArrayList; any data type can be stored in one. They also have properties and methods. The most important properties are Item and Count. Items are added to the list and removed from it. The ArrayList can be searched to see if it contains a particular item and cleared. As any data type can be stored in an ArrayList, a GetType( ) method can be used if you need to know what the data type is. A list of the more important properties and methods is shown in Table 5.1.

Property	Description
Item	Gets or set the element at the index.
Count	Gets the number of elements in the arraylist
Method	
Add	Adds an item to the end of the list
Clear	Deletes all the elements from the list
Contains	Determines if an element is in the list
Insert	Inserts an element at the specific index
Remove	Removes first occurrence of the object
ToArray	Copies the arraylist to an array

Table 5.1 ArrayList properties and methods

An exercise using the ArrayList is in the self assessment exercises

Self Assessment Exercises

1. Declare an array of 5 double values and then instantiate it using:

```
double[ ] myDblArray;
myDblArray = new double[5];
```

Write a program to fill the array with data in a 'for' loop using the .Length property.

2. Declare a string array and fill it with data in one statement using:
```
string[] myStrArray = { "str1", "str2", "str3", "str4", "str5" };
```

Write a program to display the values using a 'for' loop, then using a foreach loop (see next chapter)

3. Declare a multidimensional array of students' scores for 5 students and 3 scores.
   Hint: example code 3 students and 2 scores:

```
double [ , ] score;          // declare 2D array of double
score = new double[3,2];     // set size
```

or you can use:
```
twoDArray = new double[3, 2] { { 12, 13.1 }, { 22.1, 33.1 }, { 44.1, 55.5 } };
```

Fill the table for scores 1 and 2 for each student, and calculate the third score as 60% score1 + 40% score2.

Extend the program to display the total score (score3).

See if you can use the array method 'Average' to display the average mark.

4. Structures - 1
You might find this useful to do as we start on object oriented programming.

Create a new Windows application called Structures and place a button on the form. Declare the structure and add the button click code, so that the complete code is as follows:

```
namespace Structures
{
   public partial class Form1 : Form
   {
     struct personnelRecord
     {
        public string name;
        public int age;
        public double salary;
        public char gender;
        public personnelRecord(string name, int age, double salary, char gender)
        {
          this.name = name;
          this.age = age;
           this.salary = salary;
           this.gender = gender;
        }
     } // end declaration of struct

   private void button1_Click(object sender, EventArgs e)
   {
     personnelRecord[] PersonnelList = new personnelRecord[10];
```

```
        PersonnelList[0].name = "Freda Bloggs";
        PersonnelList[1].age = 21;
        PersonnelList[5].salary = 20000;
        PersonnelList[9].gender = 'F';
        MessageBox.Show("Name is "+PersonnelList[0].name+
          "\n\rage is "+PersonnelList[1].age+
          "\n\rsalary is "+PersonnelList[5].salary+
          "\n\rgender is "+PersonnelList[9].gender);
      } // end button click
    }
  }
```

Modify this code so that the information for each person is requested and then displayed.

Structures - 2
Create a structure for a car dealership with 3 items, Car Name (string), Car mileage (int) and Price (float).

Create an array of 5 cars and set the name, mileage and price for some of the cars.

Display all the car's information on a button click, using messageBox.Show( );

5. Strings

Declare a string called 'str29Chars' and set it to: "This string has 29 characters". Display the length of the string using the .Length property.

5.1 Use the substring method to display the first eleven characters in the string, e.g:
        MessageBox.Show(("Mary had a little lamb").Substring(0,4));
              // displays 'Mary'

5.2 Determine the starting index of the number 29 using the IndexOf( ) method, e.g:
    MessageBox.Show(("Mary had a little lamb").IndexOf("ry ha").ToString(
));
              // displays 2

5.3 Declare a new string 'str33', copy the 'str29Chars' string to it and replace the number 29 with 33 in 'str33' using the Replace( ) method, e.g:
        string strMaryText = "Mary had a little lamb";
        string strReplacedText = strMaryText.Replace("little lamb", "black sheep");

5.4 Use the .CompareTo( ) method to compare the strings 'str33' and 'str29Chars'and note the value that is returned.

6 Dynamic arrays using Arraylist

To show how we declare, add and clear and array list, try this exercise which adds an interger, a floatin point number and a string to an ArrayList and copies this to a listbox on a button click, see figure 5.3.

Start a new project and add a ListBox and two buttons on the form, label the buttons 'Add item' and 'Clear'.

Figure 5.3 ArrayList example

The complete code to declare the ArrayList and for the button clicks is as follows:

```
public partial class Form1 : Form
{
    public Form1()
    {
        InitializeComponent();
    }

    private System.Collections.ArrayList arrayOfItems
            = new System.Collections.ArrayList( );

    private void button2_Click(object sender, EventArgs e)
    {
        arrayOfItems.Clear();
    }

    private void button1_Click(object sender, EventArgs e)
    {
        Random randomNumber = new Random();      // new random number
        int rndNo = randomNumber.Next(3);        // number from 0 to 2

        switch (rndNo)                           // get random item to add
        {
            case 0: arrayOfItems.Add(randomNumber.Next(10));        // add integer
                break;
            case 1: arrayOfItems.Add(randomNumber.Next(10)*Math.PI); // add f.p
                break;
```

```
        case 2: arrayOfItems.Add("string");                  // add string
            break;
    }

    listBox1.Items.Clear( );                      // clear listbox of old items

    for (int i = 0; i < arrayOfItems.Count; i++)
    {
        listBox1.Items.Add(arrayOfItems[i]);      // add items to the listbox
    }
   }
  }
}
```

Summary

In this chapter we have looked at arrays, and seen how we declare and use single and multi-dimensional arrays. We have seen how to declare a structure, an array that contains different data types, which will lead us into object oriented code later. We have seen character arrays and strings, and some of the many string handling operations have been seen. Finally we have seen how to use dynamic arrays with the ArrayList object.

6   Program Flow, Loops and Decisions

6.1   Introduction

Sooner or later your program will need to make a decision and alter its course. There are five basic ways a C# program controls the flow of the program, they are:

- if .. else
- switch .. case
- for and foreach
- while
- do while

We shall look at each of these in turn and also look at exception handling.

6.2   The if statement

The simplest decision making construct is the 'if' statement. It takes the form of:

```
if  ( condition )
{
   statement(s)
}
```

The condition is a logical comparison which produces a true or false (a Boolean) answer. The condition must be enclosed in brackets. For example:

```
if ( bankBalance > 1000000 )
{
  MessageBox.Show ("I'm a millionaire");
}
```

If there is only one statement (as above) it doesn't need to be in curly brackets, but if there is more than one statement they must be enclosed in curly brackets, so it's good practice to use them anyway.

The logical comparisons take the following forms:

Operator	English	Example
= =	is equal to	(2+2) = = 4
!=	is not equal to	(1+2) !– 4
<	is less than	X < 2
<=	is less than or equal to	Y <= 3
>	is greater than	X > Y
>–	is greater than or equal to	(X+Y) >= Z

The test does not have to be a simple one; it can test complicated expressions so long as there is a true or false result.

6.2.1   if .. else statement

A more useful version is the if .. else , which takes the form of:

```
if ( condition )
{
  statements1
}
else
{
  statements2
}
```

Here statements1 are executed if the condition is true, and statements2 are executed if the condition is false. For example:

```
if ( expenditure > income )
{
  MessageBox.Show ("Miserable");        // if expenditure > income
}
else
{
  MessageBox.Show ("Happy");    // if expenditure =< income
}
```

You can have multiple statements (contained within curly brackets) for either of the statements.

if .. else statements can be included within other if .. else statements. In this case you can have only one ending else statement, e.g:

```
if  ( condition ) { statement(s) }
else if  ( condition ) { statement(s) }
else if  ( condition ) { statement(s) }
. .
else if  // more of the same
else  // last statement
```

6.2.2   If else shortcut

You may see the question mark and colon shortcut for if else: '? :'
For example the code:

```
if (x != 0.0)
```

```
    s = Math.Sin(x)/x;
else
    s = 1.0;
```

becomes:

```
s = x != 0.0 ? Math.Sin(x)/x : 1.0;
```

I'll let you decide which is more readable.

6.3   The switch statement

There may come a time when there you have multiple if or if.. else statements, e.g.

```
If (age == 12) { MessageBox.Show ("you are nearly a teenager") ; }
If (age == 13) { MessageBox.Show ("you are a teenager") ; }
If (age == 18) { MessageBox.Show ("you can vote") ; }
If (age == 20) { MessageBox.Show ("you are no longer a teenager") ; }
If (age == 21) { MessageBox.Show ("you're an adult – congratulations") ; }
```

The switch statement makes programming this slightly easier and more readable. The format is:

```
switch ( expression )
{
case statements
default statement
}
```

The expression must be an integer or a string which evaluates to one of the case statements. The code above would become:

```
switch ( age )
{
  case 12 :
  {
    MessageBox.Show ("You are nearly a teenager ") ;
    break ;
  }
  case 13 :
  {
    MessageBox.Show ("You are a teenager") ;
    break ;
  }
  case 18 :
  {
```

```
        MessageBox.Show ("You can vote") ;
        break ;
    }
    case 20 :
    {
      MessageBox.Show ("You are no longer a teenager") ;
      break ;
    }
    case 21 :
    {
      MessageBox.Show ("You're an adult – congratulations") ;
      break;
    }
    default :
    {
      MessageBox.Show ("You are not 12, 13, 18, 20 or 21.") ;
      break ;
    }
  }
}
```

Note the **break** statement. The break ends the **switch** code. C# does not support an implicit fall through from one case label to the next and you will get an error if the case statements do not end with a **break** or a goto statement. The one exception is if a **case** statement has no code. You can have:

```
case 6:             // no code  – will go to next case
case 7:             // no code  – will go to next case
case 8: MessageBox.Show ("executed for values of 6, 7, or 8"); break;
```

You can't have more than one condition in a case. You can't have the following:

```
case 6, 7, 8 : MessageBox.Show ("You are 6, 7, or 8") ;
          // This will error
```

You can however use the goto statement to change the flow. For instance you could have:

```
case 6:
  {
    MessageBox.Show ("You are 6");
    goto case 8;
  }
case 7:
  {
    MessageBox.Show ("You are 7");
    goto case 8;
```

```
    }
case 8:
  {
    MessageBox.Show ("executed for values of 6, 7, or 8");
    break;
  }
```

6.3.1 The goto statement

You may be surprised to see the goto statement. C# allows a goto jump to a labelled statement, but the label must be within the scope of the jump. This means you can jump out of a statement block, class or 'finally' block. However the use of goto is frowned upon as it contravenes good programming practice and makes programs difficult to understand and document.

6.3.2 Switching on a string variable

As stated earlier, you can also switch on a string variable, for example:

```
switch ( textBox1.Text )
{
  case "cut": MessageBox.Show ("cut"); break;
  case "copy": MessageBox.Show ("copy"); break;
  case "paste": MessageBox.Show("paste"); break;
}
```

6.4   Looping - The for statement

The for loop statement is used when you know the start and finish points of the loop:

```
for (variable = start expression ; end condition ; increment expression )
  {
    statement(s)
  }
```

The first expression in the statement is executed once at the beginning of the loop. The end condition determines when the loop terminates. The evaluation is performed at the beginning of each loop. Finally, the increment expression is executed each iteration of the loop. If the increment expression is an empty statement (a semicolon by itself) the loop will never terminate. You can use 'break' to terminate the loop early.

Example: Initialising an array

Suppose you wish to clear an array. A loop will easily do it. The loop code is

```
for (int count = 0 ; count <10 ; count++)
  {
```

```
        intArray [count] = 0;
    }
```

This declares and sets the loop variable 'count' to 0. It is incremented by one each time around the loop (using the short-cut '++') until the value 10 is reached. The loop will be executed ten times with count from 0 to 9. You can increment by a value other than one if you change 'count++' to say, 'count=count+3'.

Loops are often used to count through the elements in an array, or the characters in a string.

The editor automatically indents the code which helps to show the content of a loop. It is also a good idea to add a comment at the end of loops (e.g. // end of count loop). You can break out of a loop early should you need to do so, with the break statement.

Points to note:

- The loop variable can only be an integer.
- The loop variable is initialised in the for loop; you don't have to initialise it beforehand.
- The loop variable can start with any integer number.
- You should not alter the loop variable within the loop.
- The terminal value does not have to be a number; it can be a variable, say N, as long as it is defined before entering the loop.
- The loop variable may be decremented, rather than incremented, by using count-- or count=count-n

See the self assessment exercises for further loop examples

6.4.1   The foreach statement

C# also provides a 'foreach' loop. This provides a simple way to iterate through all the elements of an array or collection of objects. You do not have to specify an end condition or an increment. The following example creates an array called numbers and iterates through it with the foreach statement:

```
int[ ] numbers = { 4, 1, 6, -5, 3, 2, -2, 1, 0 };

foreach (int i in numbers)
{
    MessageBox.Show (i.ToString( ));
}
```

When this program runs it displays the values in the array, (4, 1, 6 etc.) not the value of i. This should be used for reading arrays and object data only, not setting values.

76

We saw this in the chapter on arrays, and you might like to revisit that example.

6.5 The while and do-while statements.

When the loop variable has to be changed by a varying amount or a test occurs within the loop it is better to use the while or do-while loops.

The while loop

The format of the while loop is:

```
while (expression)
{
    statement(s)
}
```

The statements will be executed while the expression is true. The expression is evaluated at the beginning of the loop.

The do-while loop

This is similar to the while loop except that the expression is evaluated at the end of the loop:

```
do
{
    statements
}
while (expression);                      // Note the semicolon
```

The do-while is convenient to use when the statements within the loop must be executed at least once. For example, when reading information from a file, keyboard or some input, you know that you will always read at least one character:

Exercise: The Fibonacci series.

The Fibonacci series occurs widely in nature and is the sum of the previous two numbers in the series starting with 0 and 1: 0, 1, 1, 2, 3, 5, 8, 13, 21 etc. The ratio of the last two numbers approaches the golden ratio (1.61803399), for example 21/13 = 1.615.

The following code displays the Fibonacci series whilst the sum is less than 10.

Place a button on a form and give it the caption: 'Fibonacci Series'
Add a list box to display the series.
Add the following code for the button:

```
private void button1_Click(object sender, EventArgs e)
{
  int old, next, sum;
  old=0;
  next=1;
  sum = old+next;
  while (sum <10)
  {
    sum=old + next;
    listBox1.Items.Add (old+" plus "+next+" is "+sum);
    old=next;
    next= sum;
  } // end of while sum<10
}
```

Run the program to display the first few numbers of the Fibonacci Series, see figure 6.1.

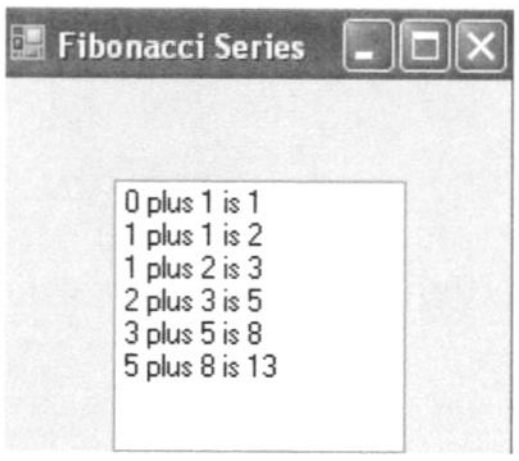

Figure 6.1 Fibonacci series

You might like to try the do.. while version:

```
int old, next, sum;
old=0;
next=1;
sum = old+next;
do
{
  sum = old + next;
  listBox1.Items.Add(old + " plus " + next + " is " + sum);
  old = next;
  next = sum;
}
while (sum < 10);    // end of do .. while sum<10
```

6.6   Exceptions. The try-catch code

Your programs may error at run-time with an exception. For instance, exceptions can happen on something as simple as a divide by zero, converting a blank textbox field into an integer, opening a file that doesn't exist, or is already in use by another application, etc. The operating system will trap exceptions, but your program should really deal with your exceptions and display relevant messages to your user.

C# provides 'try' and 'catch' code (along with 'throw' and 'finally') to deal with exceptions, trapping them out and allowing your code to deal with the exceptions. Your program can 'try' a section of code and if any exceptions occur, deal with them in the 'catch' code.

Let's see how we can trap a divide by zero error.

Exercise: Try and catch code

Start a new project and add a button to the form. Add the follow exception code to the button click:

```
int number1=123, zero = 0;
 try
 {
    number1 = number1 / zero;    // will error
 }
 catch (DivideByZeroException)
 {
    MessageBox.Show("You divided by zero!");
 }
```

You can leave out the 'DivideByZeroException' statement, and all exceptions will be trapped. There are lots of different types of exceptions. To view them all, type any letter after the opening bracket for the catch and the IntelliSense will display them, see figure 6.2.

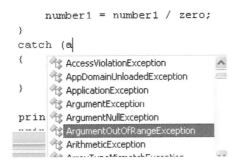

Figure 6.2 Catch exceptions

For instance, the numbers to be divided might have been read from a text box. To ensure a valid number has been entered into the text box, you could check for a FormatException as well as the DivideByZeroException as follows:

```
try
{
    int number1 = Convert.ToInt32(textBox1.Text);
    int number2 = Convert.ToInt32(textBox2.Text);
    textBox3.Text = (number1 / number2).ToString();
}
catch (FormatException)
{
    MessageBox.Show("Please check your numbers");
}
catch (DivideByZeroException)
{
    MessageBox.Show("You divided by zero!");
}
}
```

There are two extensions to the try-catch code. They are throw and finally. The throw statement passes the exception to the calling program and the finally statements are always executed and so can be used to tidy up.

Self Assessment Exercises

1. Watch the 'Using Branching and Recursion' video pointed to by Elektor's web site.

2. If exercise
Write if statements that use all of the comparison operators (==, <=, >=, etc.)
Extend this to include multiple comparisons and test your programs. For example, test for:
if integerA is greater than integerB and integerC is less than integerD, and test for:
if integerA is less than integerB or integerC is greater than integerD.

3. If then else exercise.
Write a program that requests an income value and determines the Tax due to the Government, if its tax system is as follows:
Income:
£0-1999: 0%,
£2k-2999: 10%,
£3k-39999: 22%,
Over 40k: 40%.

4. Switch exercise

Remove the default statement and complete the switch statement in section 6.3 so that a message is displayed for every teenage year. Combine years 14 to 17 so that the program drops through years 14 to 16 and displays a message for year 17: "You are between 14 and 17".

5. 'for' loop exercises:

Exercise: Two times table.

Start a new project and place a list box on a form.
Add a button and change its Caption property to 'Two Times Table'. Add the following code for the button click and run the code:

```
private void button1_Click(object sender, EventArgs e)
{
  for (int count = 1; count <= 12; count++)
  {
    listBox1.Items.Add(count+" times 2 is "+count*2);
  }          // end of for loop
}
```

```
1 times 2 is 2
2 times 2 is 4
3 times 2 is 6
4 times 2 is 8
5 times 2 is 10
6 times 2 is 12
7 times 2 is 14
8 times 2 is 16
9 times 2 is 18
10 times 2 is 20
11 times 2 is 22
12 times 2 is 24
```

More times tables
Display the three times table, starting at 1 x 3 going up to 12 x 3.
Display the four times table, starting at 12 x 4 going down to 0 x 4.

6. While loop
Declare and set an integer to zero.
Use a while loop to loop while the integer is less than 3, displaying the value in a message box. Increment the integer in the loop.

7. Do-while loop
Declare and set an integer to three.
In a do-while loop, display the integer value in a message box while the integer is more than zero. Decrement the integer in the loop.

8. Watch video lesson 11 'Handling Exceptions' pointed to by Elektor's web site.

Summary

This chapter has covered different ways of changing program flow and looping. These are the commands:

- if .. else

81

- switch .. case
- the for loop
- while
- do .. while loops.

Finally we considered exception handling code using the try-catch, throw and finally statements.

7 Object oriented programming: Methods and classes

7.1 Introduction

By now you may have realised that the programs written so far have been broken up into small portions of code, such as a button click or a timer tick event. We have used other code which we haven't written such as MessageBox.Show. Modules of code like these are called methods.

It is good practice to break your program into small parts which have a specific function and consequently are easier to get debugged and working. These smaller methods can be used in other programs, in turn making those quicker and easier to write.

If you have programmed in other languages you might call these functions, procedures or subroutines.

When we deal with object oriented code later we shall introduce classes, which are a combination of data and methods. We have already seen the DateTime and Math class and their methods (e.g. AddDays( ) and Sqrt( )).

It is useful to note that by convention, method and class names begin with a capital letter, whereas variables begin with a lower case letter. Hence just by looking at the name you can tell if it's a method or a variable. You should use this scheme for your names.

7.2 Method declaration

Let's see how we write a method and use it in our program. Our method may have data passed to it and returned from it.

A method declaration starts with the data type of the value returned, or the keyword 'void' if none, followed by the method's name, and then a list of parameters passed (with their data types and name). The method's own data and code is encased in a block within curly brackets:

return-data-type   *Method-name*   *(parameter-list in brackets)*
{
  // declarations and statements
}

As an example, let's see how we would define an integer square root method. We will pass an integer and return a double value.

The declaration starts with the return data type (double) followed by the method name (SquareRoot) and then data type of the parameters passed and a name that will be used inside the method. If there is more than one parameter, each is separated by a comma and needs its own data type.

The method's code is:

```
double SquareRoot ( int intRoot)
{
  double squareRoot = Math.Sqrt(intRoot);
  return squareRoot ;                    // squareRoot is a double data type
}
```

Note that the integer that is passed is called 'intRoot' in the method but may have another name in the calling program. The return keyword followed by the variable's name must be used to state which variable is to be passed back to the calling program.

If nothing is returned the keyword 'void' is used for the return data type in the method declaration.

We can of course declare variables to be used within our method.

To run (or call) the method from the main program, we use the method's name followed by the parameters we want to pass to it. In this case, as the method returns a value, the result will need to be assigned somewhere so it is placed after an equals sign, e.g.:

```
double dblSqRoot = SquareRoot ( integerNumber ) ;
```

You do not have to state the data type of the parameters passed when the method is called.

Exercise: A Simple method

Let's try an example before we go any further. We'll start with a method that doesn't accept or return any values. Although this may seem an odd thing to do, it might be useful if you want a method to initialise or reset all the controls on a form. We'll create a method that just waits for a short time.

Start a new windows application; call it 'Wait'. Place a button on the form and give it a suitable name (I've used btnWait). Double-click the button and change the code to be:

```
private void btnWait_Click(object sender, EventArgs e)
{
    Wait( );
}
```

To declare the Wait method, place the following code before the button click method:

```
void Wait( )
{
    int i = 0;
```

```
        while (i < 10)
          {
            i = i + 1;
          }
      }
```

Remember that even though nothing is returned, we have to state that fact using the word 'void' in the method declaration.

Run the program and click the button to call the method. Of course your computer won't wait for very long.

7.3   Parameter passing

We will want to pass data to and from our methods. For our example, we may want to wait for different amounts of time or pass a message back when it's done waiting.

Let's look at all the possibilities. We can:

1. Pass nothing, return nothing,
2. Pass something, return nothing,
3. Pass nothing, return something,
4. Pass something, return something.

The first case we have just seen. Take another look at the method declaration now 'void Wait( );' and see how the method is called using 'Wait( ); '.

Let's look at the second case and pass a variable which will be an integer value that will be used as a delay time.

Declare a new method called PassWaitingTime as follows. Add this before your 'void Wait( )' line of code.

```
        void PassWaitingTime(int delayTime)
          {
            int i = 0;
            while (i < delayTime)
            {
                  i = i + 1;
            }
          }
```

This method is passed an integer which is called delayTime within the method.

To call the method, add the following code after the Wait( ); in the button click code:

```
PassWaitingTime(100);
```

Run the code. It should wait a bit longer this time – but of course you still won't notice it.

This isn't much use if we can only pass the value of 100 each time and of course we can pass a variable.

Change the PassWaitingTime(100); to the following:

```
int longTime = 10000;
int shortTime = 10;
PassWaitingTime(longTime);
PassWaitingTime(shortTime);
```

Run the code again. This time it waits 10000 loops followed by 10 loops. You still won't notice the delay.

Note the variable name is longTime or shortTime in main program, but always called delayTime in method. You can declare a variable called delayTime in the button click, but it is different from the one in the Wait method.

What if we want to pass nothing, but return a value? Let's look at our first Wait( ) method but now return a string "done" when its finished. As this method is going to return a string, the word 'void' will be replaced by 'string' in the method's declaration. We will also have to do something with the string that is returned.

Add this method code before the void PassWaitingTime(int delayTime) code:

```
string ReturnWait( )
    {
        int i = 0;
        while (i < 10) { i = i + 1; }
        return "done";
    }
```

In our main program, let's display the string it returns. Add the following code after the Wait(shortTime); line of code in the button click:

```
MessageBox.Show(ReturnWait( ));
```

Run the code. The MessageBox.Show method will call ReturnWait and display 'done' when the waiting is over.

Finally let's pass a variable and return a value:

Add a new method PassReturnWait. (I'll let you think about where to put this)

```
string PassReturnWait(int delayTime)
    {
       int i = 0;
       while (i < delayTime)
       {
          i = i + 1;
       }
       return "done";
    }
```

And add the following code in the button click procedure:

```
shortTime = 10;
MessageBox.Show(PassReturnWait( shortTime));
```

Check that it works.

We may want to pass or return more than one value. We can pass many variables, but only return one. Parameters are passed as a list between the brackets, and we've seen an example of this in the button click method itself:

```
private void button1_Click(object sender, EventArgs e)
```

Here the object (the button) and the type of event (a mouse click mouseEvent) are passed to the method. You can test for this in the button click code, but more of that later.

7.4   Pass by reference – ref and out keywords.

In the examples we have seen, a copy of the parameter is passed to the method and the original remains intact. This is known as pass by value. However, it is possible to let the method access and permanently change the value. This is known as 'pass by reference' and the keyword 'ref' is used. The keyword 'out' is also used for methods that also initialise the variable.

If we return to our original square root example and change it to pass by reference, it becomes:

```
double SquareRoot (ref int intRoot)
{
  // code goes here
  // no return statement needed
}
```

Now neither a return statement nor an assignment statement in the main code is needed.

This becomes important if we pass an array element or a whole array to a method.

An array element is passed by value, for example if we have a method called 'Modify':

```
public void Modify (int  intModify)
  {
    intModify  = intModify *2;
  }
```

which is called by the code:

```
int [ ] intArray = { 1, 2, 3, 4, 5, 6 };
Modify (intArray[3]);
```

This does not change the original value in the array, as it was passed by value.

However, if we have a method that squares an array:

```
public void SquareArray(int[] anArray)
{
    for (int j = 0; j < anArray.Length; j++)
    {
      anArray[j] = anArray[j] * anArray[j];
    }
}
```

which is called using:

```
int[] intArray = { 1, 2, 3, 4, 5, 6 };
SquareArray(intArray);
```

The whole array is passed by reference and squared, even though the ref keyword isn't used.

7.5   Scope of a method – private and public.

As we have seen with variables, the block of code to which they are available is known as the scope. Eventually your programs will consist of many methods and classes and you may need to consider their scope. The main scope are private and public; **private** is the least permissive access level and items are accessible only within the body of the class in which they are declared; **public** is the most permissive access level, with no restrictions their access.

We shall see some other modifiers such as 'static' and 'protected' later.

7.6   Recursion

Recursive methods are ones that call themselves. This can't go on forever of course and so there must be a way of eventually stopping the recursive call, and if necessary returning a value.

Consider a method that works out the factorial of a number. The factorial of a number, N, is the multiplication of all the numbers up that number. It is denoted by N! and defined for N>0 as N! = N x (N-1)! where 1! =1.

For example the factorial of 4 is 4*3*2*1.

$$4! = 4*3! = 4*3*2! = 4*3*2*1! = 4*3*2*1.$$

A recursive method can then be defined which calls itself with a number one less than the number passed until the number is one. A method that performs this is shown below.

```
int Factorial(int factorialNo)
{
    if (factorialNo == 1)
    {
        return 1;
    }
    else
    {
        return factorialNo = factorialNo * Factorial(factorialNo - 1);
    }
}
```

The method is passed and returns an integer. The second return statement calls the Factorial method itself with the number one less than the one passed. This continues until the number 1 is passed, when the value 1 is returned. The method calls then undo themselves calculating the required value.

7.7   Calling an event

As we have seen events such as a button click are written as a method, and your program can call these methods and hence cause an event to occur, e.g. to force a button click. The correct parameters need to be passed of course.

Let's take an example. Place two buttons and a text box on a form and write the following code for the button clicks.

```
private void button1_Click(object sender, EventArgs e)
{
    textBox1.Text - "Hi there";
```

```
        }

        private void button2_Click(object sender, EventArgs e)
        {
            button1_Click(null, e);
        }
```

Now clicking button1, writes 'Hi there' into the text box. Clicking button2 calls the button1 click event to perform the same action. Note that the button click event expects an object and EventArgs data types to be passed to it (object sender, EventArgs e). You must pass (null, e) or (sender, e) to it in this case.

7.8   Classes and Namespaces

We shall see in the next chapter that a class contains both data and methods to manipulate that data, and is a template for an object. A namespace is a collection of classes and their methods.

The .NET library is composed of many namespaces. We have seen some of them such as System, System.IO, System.Windows.Forms. They are included in our program with the 'using' keyword. Namespaces are stored in dynamic link locate (DLL) files called assemblies. We shall see how to create our own DLL program and include them in our own libraries in chapter 18.

Self Assessment Exercises

1. Watch the first part of the 'Object Oriented Programming Fundamentals' video pointed to by Elektor's web site.

2. Place some text boxes on a form, and write a method that clears the text in the boxes. This method isn't passed or returns any data. Call this method from a button click and try it out.

3. Create a method that when called rolls a die (a single dice) and returns the number displayed. It's not passed anything but returns an integer value from 1 to 6.

4. Write a method that rolls a number of dice. It is passed the number of dice to roll and returns the total number thrown.

5. Write a method that rolls up to three dice. It is passed the number of dice to roll and returns a number 1 to 6 for each of the dice rolled and zero for the dice not rolled. You will have to pass four parameters and either use the out or ref keyword or pass an array.

6. Create a method that rolls a number of dice and returns the values. This time pass one variable - an array. The first value in the array holds the number of dice to roll

and the rest of the array returns the dice values.
In this case the array will be passed by reference, i.e. the whole array is passed (or more accurately the address of the array is passed). See the array examples in section 7.4 to see how a whole array is passed to a method.

7. Try writing a similar method that passes one array value only. See if the value is changed in the calling program. It shouldn't be. If you want it to be changed pass the value with the ref keyword and prove it.

8. Write a program that requests a number and calculates its factorial. Change the method so that it deals with long integer data types and large factorials.

Summary

This chapter has looked at breaking your program down into smaller more manageable parts called methods. We have seen how to declare a method and how to pass data to the method from our program and how to return values from method using the return keyword.

We have seen how to pass array elements and whole arrays to a method and discussed the ref and out keywords.

We have discussed private and public methods and recursion and also seen how we can call our events, which are methods themselves.

8 Object oriented programming – creating objects

8.1 Introduction

We have covered a lot of programming concepts so far, so now is a good time to look at Object Oriented Programming (OOP). It may seem a little early to talk about this subject so if you want to, skip this and come back, but it does fit in well with the ideas we've been covering and may actually make your programming easier.

First of all, don't panic. Object Oriented Programming was devised to relate computer programs more closely to real items such as a person, car, or house and simplify complex applications. We have seen some objects already: the button and the form are objects. We have seen that these objects have methods, properties and events. In this chapter we will see how to create our own objects.

I do not intend to cover OOP in great detail, but simply to give you an idea of how to use OOP and to create your own objects and use them.

Firstly, let's deal with some terminology.

Class
A class contains both data and methods to manipulate that data, and is a template for an object. The code and its data are integrated (or in OOP terms, *encapsulated*). The data can only be manipulated by the class code and this obviously leads to more structured and reliable code. It is from the class that we instantiate (create) our objects using the 'new' keyword, and each object is different.

Object
An object is a specific instance (or creation) of a class. You have created buttons, which are instances of class Button, and in their own right are different from each other. An object normally has its own data and the only way to change deal with that data is to use the object's own interfaces – via its own methods, properties and events.

Properties
You should be happy with properties by now. We have seen that our controls have properties and how we access the properties using the dot notation. In this chapter we will create an object with methods and properties and be able to access them with the dot notation.

Methods
We discussed methods in the previous chapter. In OOP terms you can think of a method as an action that an object can perform. In a Transport example it might be start, drive, stop, reverse etc. We call an object's method using the dot notation and if necessary pass data to the method in brackets, e.g. MessageBox.Show("message");

8.2 Creating Objects

Let's start creating our own objects. We'll create a simple object, a Point. It will have properties: X and Y. We start by writing a class which has X and Y variables and then instantiate our own Point objects based on this class. We will be able to set and read the X and Y values as properties. We'll add a Move method that will move the point. Later we'll extend this point to a new class called Circle by extending Point and adding a further property, radius.

Exercise: Our first object

Start a new Windows project and call it OOP1. Now add a new class using Project > Add Class or Project > Add New Item > Class. Give it the name Point, see figure 8.1

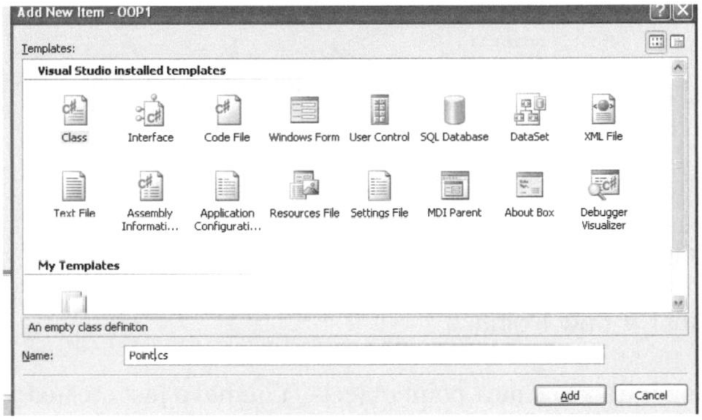

Figure 8.1 Adding a Class

If you forget to give it the name 'Point', a class called Class1 will be created. You can delete this by selecting it in the solution explorer and choosing delete.

A new tab entitled Point.cs appears in the design and has the code as follows:

```
namespace OOP1
{
    class Point
    {
    }
}
```

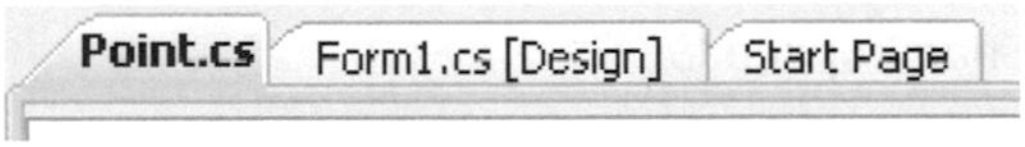

We can now create some new points from the Point class template. Return to the form design and add a button to the form. Add the following for the button click code:

```
private void button1_Click(object sender, EventArgs e)
{
    Point point1;
```

```
        point1 = new Point( );
    }
```

Notice how the IntelliSense knows about the class Point and variable point1 as you type code, see figures 8.2a and 8.2b.

Figure 8.2a IntelliSense display of class

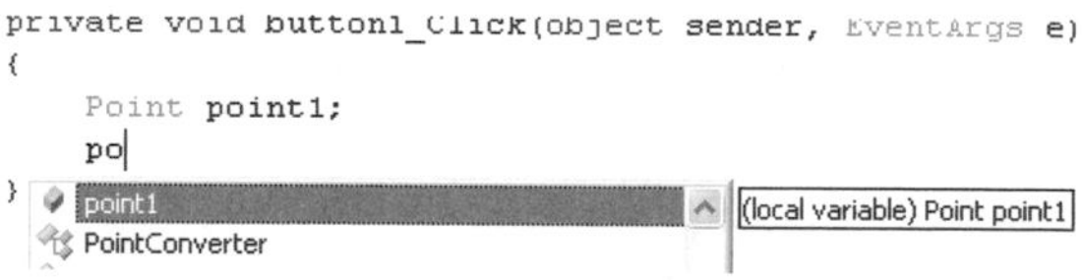

Figure 8.2b IntelliSense display of variable point1

You can also create a new object in one line of code as follows:

```
    Point point1 = new Point( );
```

Clicking the button will create new point objects. You have just created your own objects! Of course they don't do anything yet.

Let's add X and Y properties to give a position for the Point. To access them they must be declared public, but to ensure the integrity of the data there must also be internal, private variables; we shall call these _x and _y. The public X and Y properties will be accessed using the dot notation, which will in turn read and write the internal _x and _y values using 'get' and 'set' keyword methods.

Change the Point class code to the following:

```
    namespace OOP1
    {
        // Point class definition
        class Point
        {
            // private Point coordinates
            private int _x, _y;

            // constructor - runs when a new Point is instantiated
            public Point( )
            {
```

```
        }
        // property X
        public int X
        {
            // allow users to read X property – use lower case for get and set
            get {  return _x;  }

            // allow users to set X property
            set {  _x = value;  }
        } // end property X

        // ditto for property Y
        public int Y
        {
            get {  return _y;  }
            set {  _y = value;  }
        } // end property Y

    } // end class Point
}
```

Let's explain this before we run the code.

Every Point object you create will have its own private _x and _y values, these are declared with the code private int _x, _y;.

As they are declared private, they can only be accessed within the class, so to allow access using the dot notation, public properties X and Y are declared which access the private values with the get and set code:

```
        public int X
        {
            get {  return _x;  }
            set { _x = value;  }
        } // end property X
```

The get code returns the private _x variable and the set code sets private _x variable.

Note the variables X and Y have been declared public, and so can be accessed from outside of the class. Once a point has been instantiated, the dot notation code can be used, for example:

```
        firstPoint.X = 32;              // set X value
        Yposition = firstPoint.Y;       // get Y value
```

To see this in action, change the button code to the following:

```
private void button1_Click(object sender, EventArgs e)
  {
    Point firstPoint = new Point( );
    firstPoint.X = 23;
    firstPoint.Y = 345;
    int y = firstPoint.Y;
    MessageBox.Show("X value = " + firstPoint.X.ToString( ) +
      " Y value = " +    y.ToString( ));
  }
```

Run the program, the code and output should look like figure 8.3.

```
}

private void button1_Click(object sender, EventArgs e)
{
    Point firstPoint = new Point();
    firstPoint.X = 23;
    firstPoint.Y = 345;
    int y = firstPoint.Y;
    MessageBox.Show("X value = "+firstPoint.X.ToString()+" Y value = "+y.ToString());
}
```

X value = 23 Y value = 345

OK

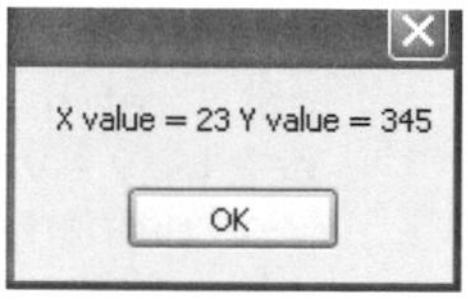

Figure 8.3 Point Class code and display

Exercise: Add more point objects

Change the button click code so that new Point objects called 'secondPoint' and 'thirdPoint' are created and then set and display their X and Y values.

8.3   Constructors

We may want a way of intialising our objects, or to set initial default values for X and Y. This is done in the constructor code and an empty constructor was included in the code you typed:

```
// constructor - runs when a new Point is instantiated
    public Point( )
    {
    }
```

The constructor is called whenever a new object is instantiated. If you don't write constructor code a default one is provided. Note the constructor has the same name as the class and even though it has no return value or type, it doesn't include the 'void' keyword.

The constructor code creates a new Point object when the following code is executed:

```
Point firstPoint = new Point( );
```

Remember the 'new' keyword is a way of making a new object from our class which is distinct from all other objects.

Now I hope you understand why we have to write this code when we create a new object and what it does. In this case it just creates the Point – it doesn't have any X or Y values at this time.

We could write code in the constructor to set X and Y to specific values, e.g. set them to zero, as follows:

```
public Point()
{
    _x = 0;
    _y = 0;
}
```

This will set the X and Y values of a new Point to zero. Change your constructor code and prove it.

We can also write constructor code that sets X and Y values points when we instantiate the object, i.e. we would write:

```
Point newPoint = new Point(123,456);
```

This will create the object with the properties passed as parameters. Our constructor code won't currently do this, and we will add another constructor to do this. This means there will be two constructors.

Before adding the code you might like to think what the second constructor contains. Consider:

a) Is the constructor code public or private?
b) What's it called?
c) What are the parameters passed (what are their type and name)?
d) What values do we set in the code?

Let's try it. Add the following code after the public Point ( ) constructor:

```
public Point(int xValue, int yValue)
{
    // set x and y
    _x = xValue;
```

```
        _y = yValue;
    }
```

We have two constructors now, one will be called with no parameters and one with X and Y parameters. The correct one will be executed depending on the number of parameters used when the object is instantiated. It is one of the features of OOP.

Add the following code for the button click and see it create the new point with the values passed:

```
Point setPoint = new Point(987,654);
MessageBox.Show("X value = " + setPoint.X.ToString( ) +
        " Y value = " +    setPoint.Y.ToString( ));

MessageBox.Show(setPoint.ToString());        // see below
```

Exercises:

- If you didn't do so, add code in the default constructor so that initial values of X and Y are set to zero.
- Take a look at the code we used when we created our structures in chapter 5.3. You can see that the personnelRecord structure has constructor code and is very similar to our class code.

8.4   The ToString method

Note the setPoint.ToString( ) method we have just used. We have used setPoint.X.ToString( ) to display the X value and setPoint.ToString( ) displays information about the object. All objects have a default .ToString() method included, without the need to write any code. At the moment, this code it simply returns 'Object.Point', see figure 8.4.

Figure 8.4 The ToString( ) method

The ToString method is defined within the original C# Object class code and we have used that code. This is called inheritance, and we shall inherit our own code and data from our Point class later.

8.5   Overriding

The ToString method doesn't provide much information. We will now write our own ToString method to provide more useful information about our class, overriding the default one.

Add the following code to the Point class (after '// end property Y'):

```
public override string ToString( )    // note the keyword 'override'
{
    return "My Point Object is at : " + _x + " " + _y;
}
```

Run the program. The message box now shows figure 8.5:

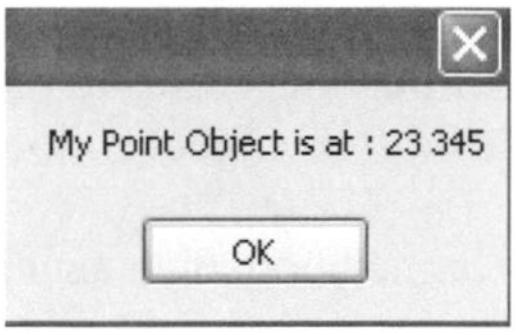

Figure 8.5 The overriden ToString( ) display

8.6   Adding Methods to a class

Apart from the ToString method, we haven't added any methods to our Point class yet. Let's now add a method called Move which moves the point a fixed distance one unit in both the X and Y directions.

We want the method to be accessible from everywhere, so it will be declared 'public'. Add the following code at the end of the Point class code, i.e. before '} // end class Point'.

```
public void Move( )  // move by one in both X and Y directions
{
    _x++;
    _y++;
} // end move
```

Add the following code to the button click code we have:

```
firstPoint.Move( );
MessageBox.Show(firstPoint.ToString( ));
```

Run the code to see that firstPoint is moved by one in the X and Y direction as shown in figure 8.6.

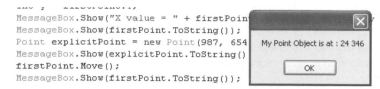

```
MessageBox.Show("X value = " + firstPoin
MessageBox.Show(firstPoint.ToString());
Point explicitPoint = new Point(987, 654
MessageBox.Show(explicitPoint.ToString()
firstPoint.Move();
MessageBox.Show(firstPoint.ToString());
```

My Point Object is at : 24 346

OK

Figure 8.6 Result of the Move method.

We can of course have private methods which would be accessible only from within our Point class.

8.7   Method overloading

As we did with the ToString method, we can also define methods with the same name but different parameters so that the method does similar (but different!) actions. This time we are declaring a second version of <u>our own</u> method and it's called method overloading. This is slightly different from overriding the ToString method, which replaced the method that was inherited from the original object code.

We shall now define a second Move method which accepts a distance to move passed to it as X and Y values.

Add the following code to the Point class

```
public void Move(int Xdistance, int Ydistance)
    {
        _x = _x + Xdistance;
        _y = _y + Ydistance;
    }
```

And add the following to the button click code, and run it to observe that the point does move.

```
firstPoint.Move(-3,345);
MessageBox.Show(firstPoint.ToString( ));
```

Notice how the intelliSense editor knows about both of the Move methods as you type, see figure 8.7.

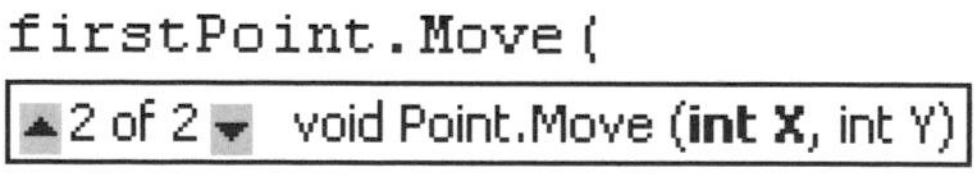

firstPoint.Move(

▲2 of 2▼ void Point.Move (**int X**, int Y)

Figure 8.7 Intellisense method display

We will add some more methods later when we have extended our Point class to a circle.

8.8 Static classes

You may have noticed that we don't have to instantiate some objects with the 'new' keyword, we can just use them. For example the Math or MessageBox classes don't have to be instantiated. They are considered to be commonly used objects and so they don't have to be instantiated before use, have been declared with the keyword 'static',

A static class is useful for methods, like the Math class, that just perform an operation or read parameters and do not use get or set.

We could do same for our Point class, but it doesn't make sense as we want to create different points. However it might be useful if we wanted a 'Distance from origin' calculation available to our objects.

We will create a new static class called Calculate to do this.

Add a new class to the project called Calculate. Within the class add a method called DistanceToOrigin. This will be our static class; note how this is declared in the code below. It will accept an X and Y position and return a double.

The complete object code is:

```
class Calculate
{
    public static double DistanceToOrigin(int x, int y)
    {
        return Math.Sqrt(x * x + y * y);
    }
}
```

Now add the following code for the button click to display the distance of our point from the origin:

```
MessageBox.Show ("Distance to Origin = "+
        Calculate.DistanceToOrigin(firstPoint.X, firstPoint.Y).ToString( ));
```

Note we do not have to instantiate Calculate or DistanceToOrigin. The result is shown in figure 8.8.

```
MessageBox.Show(firstPoint.ToString());
MessageBox.Show("Distance to Origin="+Calculate.DistanceToOri
```

Figure 8.8 Static class

8.9 Inheritance

Inheritance is a key concept in OOP. It allows you to create a new class that extends the behaviour of an existing class. We shall take our tried and tested Point code and create a new Circle class. A circle can be defined with three parameters: the X and Y point of the centre and a radius. Instead of creating a completely new Circle class which might introduce errors and take time to debug, we can use the Point class we have defined and extend it to create our Circle class. In other words the Circle object we create *inherits* the Point class's data and behaviours (and hopefully bug-free code).

To inherit from a class, the new class is defined followed by a colon and the class name to inherit from.

You've already seen this. If you look at the definition of Form1 in your C# code, you'll see a line of code similar to:

```
public class Form1 : Form
```

The Form1 : Form part indicates that your Form1 inherits from the class Form.

Exercise: A circle class

Let's add a new class called Circle. Select Project > Add class. Name it Circle.
To define a class Circle which will inherit all the Point class information, we type:

```
class Circle : Point
    {
    }
```

Change the code that has been written for you from class Circle to class Circle : Point, as above.

We can now instantiate a Circle object on the button click. To the button click code, add:

```
Circle smallcircle = new Circle( );
```

The code will run and create a circle (albeit with no radius).

What we really want is to be able to define a Radius property for our circle and add methods such as Area or Circumference. Let's add constructor code, get and set Radius property code and an Area method code. Add these to your code as follows:

```
class Circle : Point
{
    // declare an internal,private radius variable
    private double _radius;

    public Circle( ) // implict constructor call comes here
    {
    }

    public Circle(int xValue, int yValue, double radiusValue)
    {
        // Circle constructor code _x and _y obtained from Point class
        _x = xValue;
        _y = yValue;
        // _x and _y must be declared protected in Point class
        _radius = radiusValue;
    }

// property Radius
    public double Radius
    {
        get { return _radius; }
        set
        {
            if (value >= 0)    _radius = value;    // check for positive radius
        }
    }

// method Area
    public double Area()
    {
        return Math.PI * _radius * _radius;
    }

// override default ToString method
    public override string ToString( )
    {
        return "Circle at x,"+_x+" y,"+_y+" radius,"+_radius;
    }
```

}

We have now added a Radius property for the circle. However, for the Circle class to be able to access the Point variables _x and _y, their declaration has to be changed to **protected** in the Point class code. You may have noticed the error messages when you typed the code. 'Protected' is halfway between public and private declaration and allows access from with the class it is declared, but also any class derived from it.

Change the point class _x and _y declaration as follows:

```
// Point coordinates
protected int _x, _y;
```

We can now instantiate a default circle with no X,Y or Radius properties defined, or instantiate a circle with X, Y and Radius values. We can alter the X,Y and Radius properties and calculate the circle's radius. Try the following code for the button click

```
Circle smallCircle = new Circle( );            // default circle
Circle largeCircle = new Circle(12, 34, 56);   // set x,y and radius
smallCircle.X = 98;                            // set smallCircle X
smallCircle.Y = 87;                            // set smallCircle Y
smallCircle.Radius = 11;                        // set smallCircle Radius
MessageBox.Show(smallCircle.ToString( ));      // and display
MessageBox.Show(largeCircle.ToString( ));
MessageBox.Show(smallCircle.Area( ).ToString( ));
```

Notice also that your circle object has access to the Point class Move method. You can move your circle around the same way you can move your points.

8.10   Overriding methods

We have seen how we can override the ToString method. If we want to allow any of the class methods we have defined to be overridden, their declaration must be changed to **virtual**. For instance, the Area method we defined could be overridden by passing an extra parameter to calculate the volume of a cylinder.

Self Assessment Exercises

1. Watch the 'Object Oriented Programming Fundamentals' video pointed to by Elektor's web site.

2. Create a class for a Square with properties Height and Width and a method Area(). Write the code to get and set the Height and Width and calculate the Area. Provide some checks, so that negative values can't be used.

3. Create objects of your Square class (create squares) and change the square's properties in the code. Call the Area method and display it.

4. Overwrite the default .ToString() method to provide more useful information on your object.

5. Create a new class called 'Box' which inherits from Square and has an extra property 'Depth' and a new method called 'Volume' which overrides the Area method.

6. Create an object called Vehicle. It could have properties such as Bus, Car, Train, etc. Each could have a make, number of wheels and passengers etc. You could declare a public variable called 'PetrolPrice' and a static method PricePerKm.

7. Can you think how this might be overloaded to produce a Transport object with say a method PassengerPricePerKm?

8. Look at the other methods that are inherited from the Class code (Equals, GetHashCode, GetType) and find out what they mean.

9. Create a new class 'Cylinder' which inherits from the Circle and has an extra property 'Height' and method 'Volume'. Override the Area method to create a Volume method.

10. If you want to find out more about OOP, look up the terms: base class and derived class and polymorphism.

Summary

This chapter has covered writing classes and creating objects from a class. We defined a class called Point and created objects of this class using the 'new' keyword. The class has properties and methods which are parts of the object. The class properties are altered by the get and set methods and accessed from the main code using the dot notation. We have seen how an object is instantiated using a default constructor and we have created our own constructor that initialises the object's properties. The default ToString method has be overridden by our own method. We created an overloaded version of the method and seen how the methods run.

Static classes, which don't have to be instantiated, have been covered. These are useful for methods which just access values or perform calculations.

Finally, Circle objects were created from a Circle class which inherited from the Point class. To do this we had to declare protected variables and virtual methods.

9 File handling and menu dialogs

9.1 Introduction

After the fairly intensive chapter on Object Oriented Programming, let's return to more practical work.

Sooner or later you will want to save or read information on disk. Disk files are used for a wide variety of reasons; to hold temporary or permanent data, set-up or user information etc. Data logging applications can easily collect large amounts of data which may be saved on disk before analysed or transmitted elsewhere. Sometimes it is easier to save data on a disk than to deal with databases. In this chapter we will look at file types and the C# controls to handle them. We will look at databases later.

9.2 File Types – Text (ASCII) or Binary

Files are either text files (ASCII or similar) or non-text (binary) files.

9.2.1 Text Files

Text files simply contain ASCII (or UTF-8) characters, i.e. those that can be typed from the keyboard. These are often strings terminated with Carriage Return (CR, 0x0D or '\r') and Line Feed characters (LF, 0x0A or '\n'). Basic text editors create this sort of file. Most applications can handle text files and it is a good way of transferring data between applications. These files are normally handled in a line-by-line or sequential manner.

9.2.2 Binary Files - Typed and Untyped files

Binary files contain all values (i.e. printable and non-printable characters) and can't be displayed directly on the screen. Binary files are either *typed* or *untyped*. *Typed* files have a known format using data types, e.g. the structure seen in section 5.3. *Untyped* files have no rigid structure and record sizes can vary. Application (.EXE) program files and bitmap graphic files (.BMP) are good examples of these. In this case the application dealing with the file knows about the file structure and how to deal with it.

9.3 File Dialog Boxes and MenuStrip control

We shall start by looking at the C# File handling controls and Menus which make it easy to open and save files.

The .NET framework provides File and Directory classes which can be used to read and write files and these are covered later. Before that however, we shall look at the controls available to handle files.

Visual Studio environment provides dialogs to open, save and print files on the dialogs and printing toolbox. These are normally displayed using a menu system, and the MenuStrip control is used to create these. The relevant controls are shown in figure 9.1.

Figure 9.1 The MenuStrip and FileDialog controls

To open and save files, place the OpenFileDialog and SaveFileDialog controls on the form. They are non-visual controls (i.e. not part of the form), so will be placed at the bottom of the form's display area. You have used these whenever you have opened or saved files. They are displayed by executing code and we will create a menu which will do this.

9.3.1   The MenuStrip control – a simple RichTextBox editor

The MenuStrip control on the 'Menus and Toolbars' toolbox group is used to create the typical 'File, Edit, View .. Help' menu that many Windows programs have.

Let's study these with an exercise and create a simple text editor using the RichTextBox control. This application uses a MenuStrip control to display a main menu like Word with File > Open and File > Save options, and use the familiar File handling dialogs.

- Start a new Windows Application and give it a suitable name (e.g. TextEditor).
- Add the OpenFileDialog and SaveFileDialog controls to the form (they will be placed in the status area)
- Place a MenuStrip control on the form. This invites you to type a heading, see figure 9.2.

We want to have a File heading here, so type 'File'. Clicking this will allow you to type in the items for this drop down menu. Type 'Open' and 'Save'. If you hold the mouse over the menu item you will see a down arrow, which allows you to add further menu items, combo boxes, and text items or add a separator.

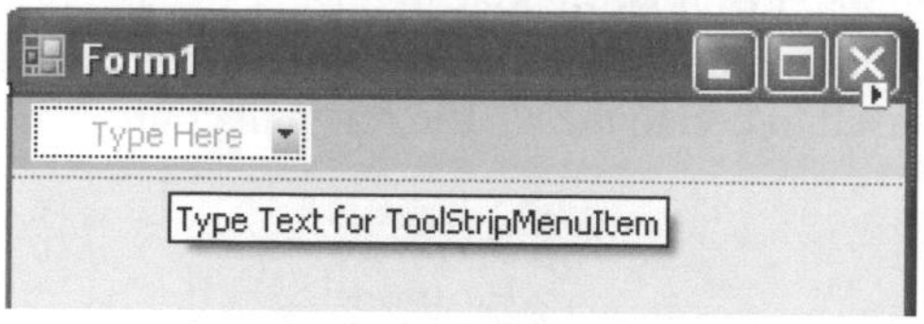

Figure 9.2 Menu Designer

- Add a separator and a File > Exit option and if you want to, a File > New option. If you make a mistake clicking away from the menu will tidy things up for you.

Let's add an Help > About menu. Add a further menu item to the right of the File menu and call it '&Help'. You will notice that the ampersand causes the 'H' in Help to be underlined and can be used as a short-cut item when your program runs.

Add an '&About' item under the Help menu.

- Finally add a Rich Text box from the Common Controls toolbox group. This is where the file that is opened will be displayed. A Rich Text box provides more functionality than a text box including edit methods such as Find, Cut, Copy and Paste, and file handling methods LoadFile and SaveFile.

Your design should be similar to figure 9.3:

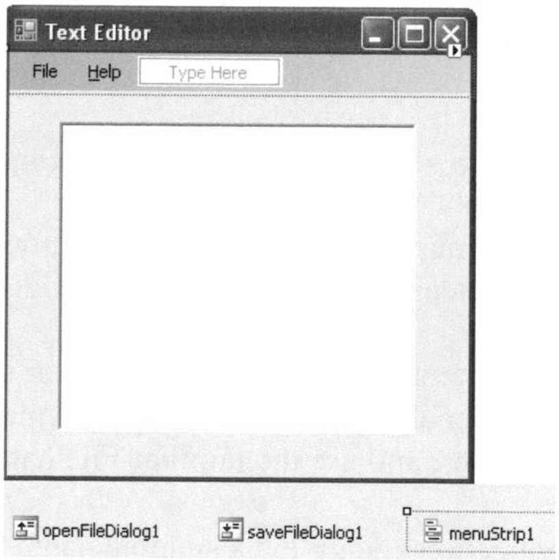

Figure 9.3 Text Editor User interface

Now we have to write the code for each of the menu items (File > Open) etc. Let's see how we can use the menu to open and save a file.

9.3.2 The OpenFileDialog

The OpenFile and SaveFile dialogs appear when an application such as Word opens or saves a file, so your user should be familiar with them, see figure 9.4. They are not permanently visible controls and appear when a 'ShowDialog' method is executed.

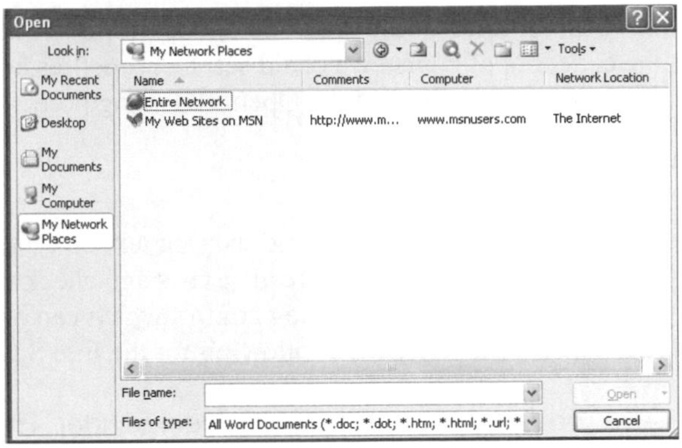

Figure 9.4 File Open Dialog

To add the File Open dialog, on the MenuStrip control click 'File' then double-click 'Open' to display the code for openToolStripMenuItem_Click.

The following code clears the richTextBox, sets up the openFileDialog properties and displays the open file dialog. Add this for the menu strip click code.

```
private void openToolStripMenuItem_Click(object sender, EventArgs e)
{
    // clear rich text box
    richTextBox1.Clear();

    // Set open file dialog initial directory and title
    openFileDialog1.InitialDirectory = @"C:\";
    openFileDialog1.Title = "Please select a file";

    // open the dialog and check for cancel
    if (openFileDialog1.ShowDialog( ) != DialogResult.Cancel)
    {
        // not cancelled - read file
        richTextBox1.LoadFile(openFileDialog1.FileName,
            RichTextBoxStreamType.PlainText);
    }
    else
    {
        MessageBox.Show("You pressed cancel");
```

}

This code sets the properties of the open file dialog and displays the dialog with the openFileDialog.ShowDialog( ) method. If the operation isn't cancelled, the file is read using the RichTextBox 'LoadFile' method.

In this example we have set up some of the open file dialog properties such as InitialDirectory in the code, but of course we could set the properties at design time. You might like to take this opportunity to look at the OpenFileDialog properties and methods.

9.3.3 The SaveFileDialog

To save the file we will use the SaveFileDialog and the rich text box method 'SaveFile'. You might want your code to check if the file already exists and check for overwriting the file. These are properties of the SaveFileDialog control which can be selected, and so we don't have to write code for them. Add the following for the File Save click:

```
private void saveToolStripMenuItem_Click(object sender, EventArgs e)
{
    if (saveFileDialog1.ShowDialog() != DialogResult.Cancel)
    {
        // not cancelled - write file
        richTextBox1.SaveFile(saveFileDialog1.FileName,
            RichTextBoxStreamType.PlainText);
    }
    else
    {
        MessageBox.Show("You pressed cancel");
    }
}
```

Finally, for the File > Exit commands add the following code:

```
private void exitToolStripMenuItem_Click(object sender, EventArgs e)
{
    Application.Exit( );
}
```

Save the project and run the program. Select a text (.TXT) file to see it displayed in the list box. You can save the file under another name, or change the text in the memo box and save it. You have created a simple editor.

If you want to see how a binary file is displayed, try selecting an Application (.EXE) file.

9.3.4 Open and Save Dialog Box properties

At this stage, the dialog boxes display all the file types. You might want to limit the file types that the user can see. It's not really necessary for our editor program to display anything other than text files and possibly 'All files'. To select specific files such as *.TXT, the filter property is used. The filter can be set in the properties or by code. To select files in code, try the following code:

openFileDialog1.Filter = "All files (*.*)|*.*|Text files(*.TXT)|*.txt";

You can try adding word documents (*.DOC) and open one to see how it's displayed.

Repeat for the Save Dialog component and save the project. You can now run the program. Selecting File > Open will display the Open Dialog box, only text (.TXT) files only are shown and can be selected.

Save the file with a different name and directory. Close the application using File > Exit and using your favourite editor, prove to yourself that the file has indeed been copied to a different directory.

9.3.5 File error handling

Currently, if the user types in an invalid filename rather than selecting one from the folder, an error message is shown. Setting the CheckFileExists property of the OpenFileDialog control to 'true' will prevent this. There are many other properties which you might find useful to try out, including 'CheckPathExists', 'DefaultExt' and 'AddExtension' (you might like to add the extension TXT and see what happens).

Remember you can put your file handling code in a try-catch block (see chapter 6) which can deal with errors that may occur.

9.4   Adding Menu items – About box

The Help > About menu item hasn't been added. Let's do that. An About form is one of the forms available from the Form menus.

Select Project> Add Windows Form and select About Box from the offerings. An About Box is displayed, which you can modify to suit, Figure 9.5.

Figure 9.5 The About Box

The About box does not display the changes made at design time to the About box form. Although the About box is initialised correctly, the compiler then uses the project's assembly information and overwrites these changes. This code is in AboutBox1.cs:

```
public AboutBox1()
{
    InitializeComponent();
    this.Text = String.Format("About {0} {0}", AssemblyTitle);
    this.labelProductName.Text = AssemblyProduct;
    this.labelVersion.Text = String.Format("Version {0} {0}",
AssemblyVersion);
    this.labelCopyright.Text = AssemblyCopyright;
    this.labelCompanyName.Text = AssemblyCompany;
    this.textBoxDescription.Text = AssemblyDescription;
}
```

The assembly information is held in AssemblyInfo.cs, but you should not change that code. If you want to create your form at design time, you can comment out the lines beginning with 'this' in the above code.

More correctly you should change the project assembly information using Project > Application > Assembly Information as shown in Figure 9.6.

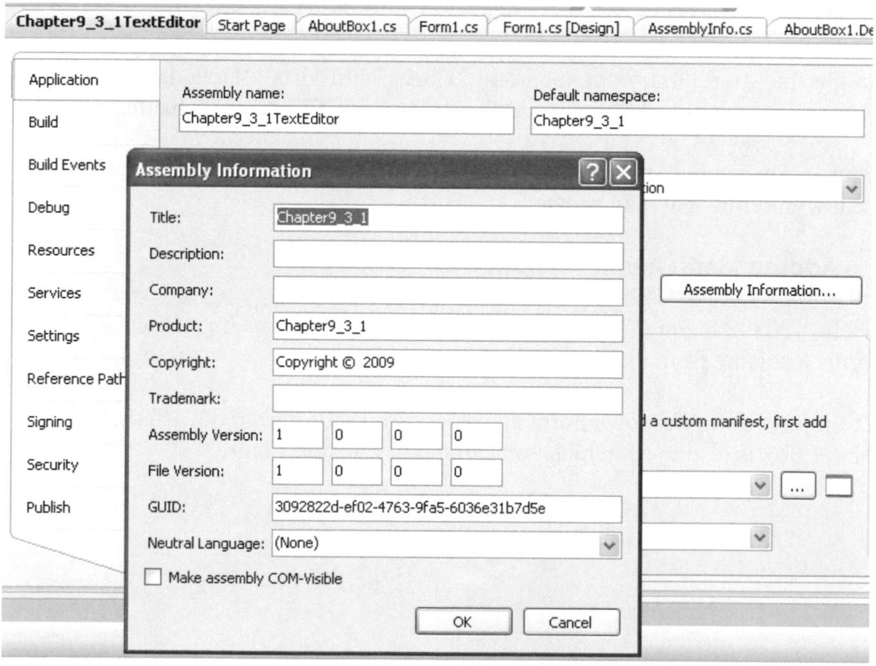

Figure 9.6 Assembly Information

Finally, the OK button doesn't automatically close the About box. You need to write code to do that. Double-click the OK button and change the code to the following:

```
private void okButton_Click(object sender, EventArgs e)
{
    this.Close();
}
```

9.5   PrintDialog boxes

A file can be printed using the PrintDialog and PrintDocument controls found on the Printing toolbox controls. The PrintDialog requests the printer you want to use, the page range, number of copies, etc and is displayed with the ShowDialog() method. The PrintDocument contains the event that prints the document.

If you want further information on this, search Help for the PrintDocument Class.

9.6   RichTextBox editor: cut, paste copy and find

The rich text box also has methods for cut, copy and paste. All you have to do is add menu items for these, e.g. Edit> Cut and Edit >Paste, and add the following code:

```
private void cutToolStripMenuItem_Click(object sender, EventArgs e)
{
    richTextBox1.Cut();
}

private void pasteToolStripMenuItem_Click(object sender, EventArgs e)
{
    richTextBox1.Paste();
}
```

Run your program, type some text into the rich text box and select some of it. Edit > Cut will remove the selection and Edit > Paste will replace it. Edit > Copy works in a similar way.

For the Find, you have to choose the text to find. Add an Edit > Find menu item and the following code for the click event. The code finds the text 'Text', matching its case and changes the selection to Verdana, 12, italic, blue.

```
private void findToolStripMenuItem_Click(object sender, EventArgs e)
{
    richTextBox1.Find("Text",RichTextBoxFinds.MatchCase);
    richTextBox1.SelectionFont = new Font ("Verdana", 12, FontStyle.Italic);
    richTextBox1.SelectionColor = Color.Blue;
}
```

9.7 File and Directory classes

Your program might not need to request file details from the user and you can use the File and Directory classes. These provide static methods for the creation, copying, deletion, moving, and opening of files.

The FileStream class is used to read from, write to, open, and close files on a file system, and is specified when the filestream is instantiated.

The encoding of different data types is performed using StreamReader and StreamWriter classes in the case of text files (utf-8), and BinaryWriter and BinaryReader classes in the case of binary data.

The main File methods are:

AppendText	Creates a StreamWriter that appends text to an existing file.
Copy	Copies an existing file to a new file.
Create	Creates a file in the specified path.
Delete	Deletes the specified file.
Exists	Determines whether the specified file exists.
Open	Opens a FileStream on the specified path.
OpenRead	Opens an existing file for reading.
OpenText	Opens an existing text file for reading.
OpenWrite	Opens an existing file for writing.
ReadAllBytes	Opens a binary file, reads the file into a byte array and closes the file.
ReadAllLines	Opens a text file, reads all its lines into a string array and closes the file.
ReadAllText	Opens a text file, reads all lines of the file into a string and closes the file.
Replace	Replaces the contents of the file with the contents of another file, deleting the original file and creating a backup of the replaced file.
WriteAllBytes	Creates a new file, writes the specified byte array to the file and then closes the file. If the target file exists, it is overwritten.
WriteAllLines	Creates a new file, writes the specified string to the file and then closes the file. If the target file exists, it is overwritten.
WriteAllText	Creates a new file, write the contents to the file and closes the file. If the target file exists, it is overwritten.

The main Directory methods are:

CreateDirectory	Creates all the directories in a specified path.
Delete	Deletes a specified directory.
Exists	Determines whether the directory exists.
Move	Moves a file or a directory and its contents to a new location.

Remember to add 'using System.IO' if you want to use these classes.

114

9.8 File handling example

Here are two examples of writing and reading to files using the File and Directory classes. The first uses StreamWriter and StreamReader classes to create a text file and read it back, and the second uses File and Directory classes to check if they exist and then FileStream, BinaryWriter and BinaryReader to write binary data to a file, then read it back:

9.8.1 Using StreamWriter and StreamReader objects

The following example creates a StreamWriter object to write text to a file and then creates a StreamReader object to read it.

```
StreamWriter sw = new StreamWriter("Test.txt");
// Add some text to the file.
sw.Write("Hello ");           // no CRLF
sw.WriteLine("World!");       // add CRLF
sw.WriteLine("-------------------");
sw.Close();

// The using statement also closes the StreamReader.
using (StreamReader sr = new StreamReader("Test.txt"))
{
    MessageBox.Show(sr.ReadLine());   // Hello world!
    MessageBox.Show(sr.ReadLine());   // -----------
}
```

The file can be checked by reading it in Notepad.

9.8.2 Using BinaryReader and BinaryWriter objects.

The following example creates a BinaryWriter object to write binary values text to a file and then creates a BinaryReader object to read the data.

```
string dirPath = @"c:/Temp";

// Create the folder c:\temp if it doesn't exist

if (!Directory.Exists(dirPath))
{
    Directory.CreateDirectory(dirPath);
}

string fileName = @dirPath + "/TestFile.bin";
// create and binary file if it doesn't exist
if (!File.Exists(fileName))
```

```
        {
            // file doesn't exist - create file

            FileStream fs = new FileStream(fileName, FileMode.CreateNew);
            BinaryWriter bw = new BinaryWriter(fs);
            byte[] byteArray = { 0x48, 0x45, 0x4C, 0x4C, 0x4F }; // hello!

            for (int i = 0; i < byteArray.Length; i++)
            {
                bw.Write(byteArray[i]);
            }

            bw.Close();
            fs.Close();
        }

        // and read it back

        FileStream fsRead = new FileStream(fileName, FileMode.Open);
        BinaryReader br = new BinaryReader(fsRead);

        for (int i = 0; i < fsRead.Length; i++)
        {
            MessageBox.Show(br.ReadByte().ToString());
        }

        br.Close();
        fsRead.Close();
```

Note that as this file contains ASCII characters for HELLO, it can also be read by notepad.

Self Assessment Exercises

1. Add Print commands to the menu strip and your editor. If you need more information try searching in Help.

2, Add the cut, copy, paste commands to your editor.

3. Add Find and Replace commands to your editor.

4. Write a program to open a text file and save the individual high and low 4 bit nibbles of each byte and in a binary file. Write a program to do the reverse, i.e. reads two bytes from a binary file, combines them and writes them as a text file.

Summary

In this chapter we have looked at text and binary file types. We have seen the MenuStrip component and looked at the openFileDialog and saveFileDialogs. A simple editor was created using the versatile rich text box to load and save files. The editor was extended to provide print, cut, paste and find commands. Finally we looked at File and Directory classes and saw how to read and write both text and binary files using StreamWriter and StreamReader classes and FileStream, BinaryWriter and BinaryReader classes.

10 Graphics and Multimedia

10.1 Introduction

Your user interface can be made more impressive if it uses images and graphics. We have seen the picture box control which can display images. There are no graphics controls such as rectangle or ellipse that can be placed directly on the form; they have to be drawn by your code. In this chapter we will see how to draw graphics objects. We shall also look at the Media Player control.

10.2 Drawing Graphics

The basic procedure for drawing text or graphics is as follows: A Graphics object is created on a form or container such as a panel where the graphics is to be drawn. A pen or brush object is defined, and then Graphics methods are called to draw or paint lines and shapes. The pen is used to draw lines and the brush to fill areas. The Graphics object is in the System.Drawing namespace.

Exercise: Line Drawing.

Let's see how we draw lines with an example that draws a line on a panel on a form.

Start a new application and place a panel on the form. So you can see the panel, change its BorderStyle property to FixedSingle. Find the panel's MouseDown event and change it to the following code:

```
private void panel1_MouseDown(object sender, MouseEventArgs e)
{
    System.Drawing.Graphics grpObject;
    grpObject = this.panel1.CreateGraphics( );
    Pen objmyPen = new Pen(System.Drawing.Color.Blue);
    grpObject.DrawLine(objmyPen, 0, 0, 100, 100);
}
```

In this code the graphics object (grpObject) is created on panel1. A Pen object is created (objmyPen) in Blue. Note the American spelling for colour. The DrawLine method uses the Pen object to draw between two x and y points. In this case from 0, 0 to 100, 100.

Run the program and click on the panel. A blue line should be drawn from top left to bottom right of the panel as shown in figure 10.1. Note that point (0,0) is the top left, with increasing X values moving right and increasing Y values moving down the screen.

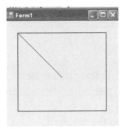

Figure 10.1 Drawing on a panel

10.3   The Paint event.

Unfortunately the line doesn't stay drawn if the form is minimized or hidden and then redisplayed. In this example the line is only drawn when the panel is clicked and not when the panel is redisplayed. We need to draw the line when our form is redrawn. The panel and the form controls have a paint event which occurs when the control is redrawn. We will now use this event to draw a line.

Find the paint event for the panel in the properties window and change it to the following code:

```
private void panel1_Paint(object sender, PaintEventArgs e)
{
   // draw red line
   System.Drawing.Graphics grpObject = e.Graphics;
   Pen objmyPen = new Pen(System.Drawing.Color.Red);
   grpObject.DrawLine(objmyPen, 0, 100, 100, 0);
}
```

Run the code. When the panel is drawn, its Paint event occurs and a red line is drawn on the panel from bottom left to top right. Click the panel to draw the blue line. Now minimize and redisplay the form; the original blue line disappears, but the red line is still drawn by the paint event.

Note in this case how the graphics object (e.Graphics) was obtained from the PaintEventArgs parameter passed to the panel's paint event.

You should dispose of your objects when you have finished with them. To do so use the code:

```
objmyPen.Dispose( );
```

If you need to redraw your graphics from your code you should not call the Paint event, but instead call the Invalidate method. This invalidates the object which will then be redrawn by Windows:

```
panel1.Invalidate( );
```

10.4   Drawing on the form

When the form is opened or revealed, the objects on it are drawn by the paint event. You can prove this by displaying a message with MessageBox.Show in the Form_Paint event. If you wish to draw on your form you can either add code to this event or you can write your own OnPaint event, overriding the original.

For example, add the following OnPaint method

```
protected override void OnPaint(PaintEventArgs e)
{
    Graphics grpObject = e.Graphics;
    Pen objmyPen = new Pen(System.Drawing.Color.Blue);
    grpObject.DrawLine(objmyPen, 0, 0, 100, 100);
}
```

The Paint event (now your OnPaint code) is triggered when the form is opened or displayed and hence the graphics is drawn every time; it doesn't disappear. Note however, that resizing the form doesn't trigger the form's Paint event.

You can still call the original Paint code from your OnPaint method if you add the following code:

```
base.OnPaint(e);
```

In this code the term 'base' refers to the base class, in this case the Form. This code calls the form's original Paint code, which we have just overridden.

If you want to prove it, add MessageBox.Show("In form's paint"); code to the form's Paint event and see what happens. The message only appears if the base.OnPaint(e); code is present and appears when the form is resized or redisplayed.

If you need your graphics to stay on the form then you can do it in one of two ways:

- Place all the code in the form's Paint event. This is best if you are drawing only a few items.
- Draw to a memory bitmap and copy the bitmap to the form in the form's Paint event. This is more complicated and better if you are doing a lot of drawing, but beyond the scope of this book.

10.5   The Pen

As we have seen, the Pen is used to draw lines and we shall use it to draw shapes such as rectangles, circles, ellipses and polygons later. A Pen object is created and it controls the appearance of the lines drawn. The main Pen properties are:

- Color - This is specified by setting the individual values for Alpha, Red, Green and Blue (ARGB). Alpha defines the transparency of the colour and is optional. Each ARGB value can be from 0 – 255. For the RGB values 0, 0, 0 is black and 255, 255, 255 is white.
- Width - The width in pixels of the line drawn.
- DashStyle - Specifies the pattern of the line (Solid, Dash, Dot, DashDot, Custom, etc.)

Once a pen object has been created its colour, width, style etc can be changed as shown in the following example code fragment:

```
System.Drawing.Graphics grpObject;
grpObject = this.panel1.CreateGraphics();
 // create blue pen 5 pixels wide
Pen objmyPen = new Pen(System.Drawing.Color.Blue, 5);
grpObject.DrawLine(objmyPen, 0, 0, 100, 100);

// chage Width
objmyPen.Width = 3;

// chage style to dashed
objmyPen.DashStyle =
        System.Drawing.Drawing2D.DashStyle.DashDotDot;

// change to semi-transparent red
objmyPen.Color = System.Drawing.Color.FromArgb(128, 255, 0, 0);
grpObject.DrawLine(objmyPen, 0, 100, 100, 0);
```

Note that the FromARGB( ) method has been used to set the alpha and RGB values. The program output is shown in figure 10.2.

Figure 10.2 Pen drawing program output

10.6   The Brush

The brush object defines how areas are filled. Like the Pen, the brush object has to be created and its main properties are its colour and style.

- The Color determines the colour of the filled shapes, including foreground and background colours.
- The Style determines if the area is filled with a solid colour or a line style. Some styles are:
  HatchBrush (uses a foreground and background colour),
  LinearGradientBrush (blends one colour into another),
  SolidBrush (fills with one colour),
  TextureBrush (uses an Image).

10.7   Drawing Text

Text is drawn with DrawString( ) method. You state the text string, the font and brush style together with the X and Y position of the text, for example:

```
private void panel1_Paint(object sender, PaintEventArgs e)
{
  Graphics grpObject = e.Graphics;
  Font myFont = new Font("Arial", 16);
  SolidBrush myBrush = new SolidBrush(Color.Green);
  grpObject.DrawString("Mystring", myFont, myBrush, 20, 30);
}
```

10.8   Basic Shapes

Methods are provided for graphics objects to draw ellipses and rectangles (and hence circles and squares). Having created a graphics object as we did above, the methods can be used. We have seen the DrawString( ) method. You can let the Intellisense prompt display them, see figure 10.3.

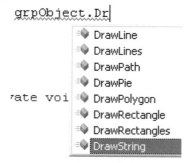

Figure 10.3 Graphics object drawing methods

Other basic graphic methods are:

DrawRectangle (Pen p, int X, int Y, int width, int height);

This draws a rectangle with pen p, at X, Y, with width and height.

DrawEllipse (Pen p, int X, int Y, int width, int height);

This draws an ellipse with Pen p, bounded by the rectangle defined by top left hand point X, Y with width and height.

FillRectangle (Brush b, int X, int Y, int width, int height);

This draws a filled rectangle with brush b, bounded by the rectangle defined by top left hand point X, Y with width and height.

FillEllipse(Brush b, int X, int Y, int width, int height);

This draws a filled ellipse with brush b, bounded by the rectangle defined by top left hand point X, Y with width and height.

For more detail on drawing shapes, refer to the self assessment exercises. This has an example which draws a different shape and colour each time the form is painted as shown in figure 10.4.

Figure 10.4 Shape program output

Reading and writing a single pixel

There is no graphics command to read or write a single pixel. You could draw a line from x,y to x,y+1, but that draws two pixels.

To read or write to a pixel on the screen you have to import some DLL methods from gdi32 (see chapter 18.6). The calls are CreateDC, DeleteDC, SetPixel and GetPixel.

To draw to the screen you have to 'borrow' it from Windows. To do this you have to create a device context (using CreateDC) and return it when finished (using DeleteDC). CreateDC returns a pointer to the drawing object, which is then used by SetPixel and GetPixel.

The following code example displays the colour value of a panel when it is clicked and then generates a new random background colour for it.

At the top of your code, add the declaration 'using System.Runtime.InteropServices;'

Add the following DLLImport code before 'public Form1':

```
// DLL to create a device context for a resource.
[DllImport("gdi32.dll")]
public static extern IntPtr CreateDC(string strDriver, string strDevice,
string strOutput, IntPtr pData);

// DLL to release the resource
[DllImport("gdi32.dll")]
public static extern bool DeleteDC(IntPtr hdc);

// DLL to set a pixel - pass DC pointer, x, y and colour
[DllImport("gdi32.dll")]
static extern uint SetPixel(IntPtr hdc, int X, int Y, uint crColor);

// DLL to get pixel value - pass DC pointer, x and y, colour value is
returned
[DllImport("gdi32.dll")]
public static extern uint GetPixel(IntPtr hdc, int nXPos, int nYPos);
```

Place a panel on a form and enter the following code for its mouse down event:

```
private void panel1_MouseDown(object sender, MouseEventArgs e)
{

// Obtain a Device Context for the panel.
IntPtr ptrScreen = CreateDC("Display", null, null, IntPtr.Zero);

// and use it to obtain the pixel value of the mouse position
// GetPixel
int pixelValue = (int)GetPixel(ptrScreen, e.X, e.Y);

// and release it
DeleteDC(ptrScreen);

// Convert the pixel value colour to a .NET Color object

Color clr = Color.FromArgb((pixelValue & 0x000000FF),
  (pixelValue & 0x0000FF00) >> 8,
  (pixelValue & 0x00FF0000) >> 16);
```

```
    string str = "red: " + clr.R +" green: " + clr.G + "blue: " + clr.B;
    MessageBox.Show(str);

    // generate new panel background colour
    Random rndObj = new Random();
    int red = rndObj.Next(255);
    int green = rndObj.Next(255);
    int blue = rndObj.Next(255);
    panel1.BackColor = Color.FromArgb(red, green, blue);
}
```

Note the use of e.X and e.Y from MouseEventArgs to obtain the X and Y position of the mouse.

Color.FromArgb creates a Color structure, clr, from the 8-bit alpha, red, green, and blue pixel values. Here we only use RGB. Note that having got a Color value, you can extract the individual ARGB values – note the use of clr.R, clr.G and clr.B. The program creates the new background colour using Color.FromArgb from three random values.

You can also set a pixel in the same way. The following code snippet writes to the screen on the panel's mouse move event. Note that the X and Y positions are obtained from the panel, and they are used as X and Y positions to write to the screen (not the panel).

```
    private void panel1_MouseMove(object sender, MouseEventArgs e)
    {
      Random rndObj = new Random();
      int red = rndObj.Next(255);
      int green = rndObj.Next(255);
      int blue = rndObj.Next(255);
      // Obtain a Device Context for the Display.
      IntPtr ptrScreen = CreateDC("Display", null, null, IntPtr.Zero);
      // and use it to obtain the pixel value of the mouse position

      // SetPixel
      SetPixel(ptrScreen, e.X, e.Y, (uint)((red << 16) | (green << 8) | (blue)));
      // and release resource
      DeleteDC(ptrScreen);
    }
```

10.9   Other shapes – arcs, pies, polylines and polygons.

Other shapes such as arcs, pie, filled pie, polylines, polygons and filled polygons can also be drawn. The basic graphic methods for these are defined as follows. They can also be overridden, so there are many variants.

DrawArc(Pen p, int X, int Y, int width, int height, int startAngle, int sweepAngle);

This uses the Pen and draws an arc of an ellipse from startAngle in degrees, sweeping by sweepAngle, bounded by the rectangle defined by top left hand point X, Y with width and height.

Arcs sweep in a clockwise manner, with 0^0 being along the +X-axis.
 DrawPie (Pen p, int X, int Y, int width, int height, int startAngle, int sweepAngle);

This draws a pie section with the same parameters as the DrawArc.

FillPie (Brush b, int X, int Y, int width, int height, int startAngle, int sweepAngle);

Similar to DrawPie, except a filled Pie is drawn using the brush.

Polylines and Polygons (a closed series of Polylines) are best drawn using the Polyline and Polygon methods. These methods draw a series of lines connecting points which are passed to the method in an ArrayList. A filled polygon can also be drawn using the FillPolygon method.

The self assessment exercises have an example on drawing Polygons. In the exercise the user clicks the mouse to define the X and Y positions for the polygon's points, and produces a display similar to figure 10.5.

Figure 10.5 Polygon program output

10.10 Drawing Graphs and Charts

If you want to draw a graph or chart, you can either draw your own or obtain some third party software. We will study drawing graphs using a third party package called NPlot in chapter 17.

If you want a simple 2D chart, there is an example at the Coding4Fun site at:
http://msdn.microsoft.com/coding4fun/someassemblyrequired/hotinhere/default.aspx

126

Some free chart controls are also available. If you need these, you can try:
http://www.carlosag.net/Tools/WebChart/Default.aspx

10.11 Multimedia applications

The MediaPlayer control is used to control playing or recording devices such as audio or video CD-ROM/DVD player.

The MediaPlayer control, see figure 10.6, provides a screen and controls to manage the media (play, pause, stop, etc.)

Figure 10.6 MediaPlayer control

To use the media player control, it first has to be added to the toolbox. The process is described here, but is also on the Microsoft site at:
http://windowssdk.msdn.microsoft.com/en-us/library/ms750211.aspx.

Start a new project and Right-click toolbox and select 'choose items'. Choose toolbox items displays select COM controls tab. Click Windows Media Player. (If it does not appear, browse for wmp.dll in your Windows > System folder). Click OK to add the control to the toolbox.

Add the Player to the form and resize it to show the controls and the screen. Its default name is 'axWindowsMediaPlayer1'.

Add a button and change its Text to 'Load Video'. Add the following code for the click event:

```
axWindowsMediaPlayer1.URL = @"c:\windows\clock.avi";
```

The @ symbol instructs the compiler to ignore backslashes which would otherwise be interpreted as an escape sequence. Make sure the file exists. You could add a file dialog box to search for media files. Because the autoStart property is true by default, the media will start when you set the URL.

Your GUI should be similar to figure 10.7:

Figure 10.7 The MediaPlayer GUI

You can control the video from your application, for example you could have:

```
axWindowsMediaPlayer1.Ctlcontrols.stop( );
```
or
```
axWindowsMediaPlayer1.Ctlcontrols.play( );
```

If you want to distribute your multimedia application, you need to add a couple of files to your application. See the above reference for more details.

If you don't want the player controls to be displayed, set the uiMode property to 'none'. You can also turn the screen off if by making it invisible. E.g:

```
axWindowsMediaPlayer1.uiMode = "none";
axWindowsMediaPlayer1.uiMode = "invisible;
```

You can also have a mini or custom controls display.

Note: if you copy the multimedia file to your program folder, you can move files between computers if you use relative addressing and change the filename's drive (C:) and path (..\Demos\etc.)

10.11.1   MediaPlayer events

If you want to loop your sound or video, you have to detect the event which tells you the media has finished playing and restart your media. Find the PlayStateChanged event and add the following code to loop the media:

```
private void axWindowsMediaPlayer1_PlayStateChange
  (object sender, AxWMPLib._WMPOCXEvents_PlayStateChangeEvent e)

    {
       axWindowsMediaPlayer1.Ctlcontrols.play();
    }
```

Self Assessment Exercises

Try the following exercises

1. The Paint method

Place a panel on the form. Add MessageBox.Show methods to the panel's paint event and the form's paint event and observe the paint's operation. Override the form's paint event with your own OnPaint method, which should also have a MessageBox.Show method. Notice that the original form's paint method no longer runs. Add a base.OnPaint(e); code and see that the form's paint method is now called.

2. Drawing shapes

As an exercise in drawing the different shapes, type in the following code for the form's OnPaint overridden event. It draws a different shape and colour each time the form is painted as shown in figure 10.5.

```
protected override void OnPaint(PaintEventArgs e)
{
    Graphics grpObject = e.Graphics;            // create Graphics object
    Pen objmyPen = new Pen(System.Drawing.Color.Blue);     // define Pen
    SolidBrush myBrush = new SolidBrush(Color.Red);        // and brush
    Font arial = new Font("Arial", 12);                    // and font

    Random RandomNumber =  new Random();   // define random number
    int rndNo = RandomNumber.Next(4);      // get random value 0 to 3

    switch (rndNo)                         // get random brush color
    {
        case 0: myBrush.Color = Color.Red; break;
        case 1: myBrush.Color = Color.Blue; break;
        case 2: myBrush.Color = Color.Orange; break;
        case 3: myBrush.Color = Color.Green; break;
    }

    rndNo = RandomNumber.Next(4);          // get random value 0 to 3
    switch (rndNo)                         // get random pen color
    {
        case 0: objmyPen.Color = Color.DarkOrchid; break;
        case 1: objmyPen.Color = Color.Tomato; break;
        case 2: objmyPen.Color = Color.Peru; break;
        case 3: objmyPen.Color = Color.AliceBlue; break;
    }
```

```
rndNo = RandomNumber.Next(7);              // get random number 0-6
int rndX = RandomNumber.Next(100);          // get random X and Y
int rndY = RandomNumber.Next(100);          // values for end point
string drawnstr=null;                       // string for DrawString

switch (rndNo)                              // draw random shape at 0,0
{
    case 0:                                             // draw line
        grpObject.DrawLine(objmyPen, 0, 0, (float)rndX,(float)rndY);
        drawnstr = "Line to ";
        break;
    case 1:                                             // draw rectangle
        grpObject.DrawRectangle(objmyPen, 0, 0, (float)rndX, (float)rndY);
        drawnstr = "Rectangle ";
        break;
    case 2:                                             // fill rectangle
        grpObject.FillRectangle(myBrush, 0, 0, (float)rndX, (float)rndY);
        drawnstr = "Filled rectangle to ";
        break;
    case 3:                                             // draw ellipse
        grpObject.DrawEllipse(objmyPen, 0, 0, (float)rndX, (float)rndY);
        drawnstr = "Ellipse to ";
        break;
    case 4:                                             // fill ellipse
        grpObject.FillEllipse(myBrush, 0, 0, (float)rndX, (float)rndY);
        drawnstr = "Filled ellipse to ";
        break;
    case 5:                                             // draw square x = y
        grpObject.DrawRectangle(objmyPen, 0, 0, (float)rndX, (float)rndX);
        drawnstr = "Square to ";
        break;
    case 6:                                             // draw circle x = y
        grpObject.DrawEllipse(objmyPen, 0, 0, (float)rndX, (float)rndX);
        drawnstr = "Circle to ";
        break;
} // end switch

// draw string
grpObject.DrawString((drawnstr + rndX + "," + rndY),
        arial, myBrush, 0, 100);
base.OnPaint(e);    // call form's paint event
}
```

3. Drawing Polygons

Let us study a filled polygon example. In this example the polygon is drawn as the user clicks on a panel. The mouse X and Y coordinates are added to an ArrayList and the panel is invalidated to force a redraw. Refer to Chapter 5, Arrays and Strings, for more details of the ArrayList.

Start a new project and place a panel on the form. We shall draw the polygon on the panel. Place a button labeled 'Reset' on the form.

Add the following code for the panel's mouseDown event, the paint event and the button click event, so the complete code is as follows:

```
namespace Polygon
{
    public partial class Form1 : Form
    {
        public Form1()
        {
            InitializeComponent();
        }

        private System.Collections.ArrayList aryPoints =
            new System.Collections.ArrayList();
        SolidBrush myBrush = new SolidBrush(Color.Gold);

        private void panel1_MouseDown(object sender, MouseEventArgs e)
        {
            aryPoints.Add(new Point(e.X, e.Y));
            // x and y postion of mouse passed
            panel1.Invalidate();
            // Invalidate to call panel's paint event
        }

        private void panel1_Paint(object sender, PaintEventArgs e)
        {
            Graphics myGrpObject = e.Graphics;
            // get panel's graphics object
            if (aryPoints.Count > 1)
            // 2 points or more - draw shape
            {
                Point[ ] arrayofPoints =
                    (Point[ ])aryPoints.ToArray(aryPoints[0].GetType( ));
                myGrpObject.FillPolygon(myBrush, arrayofPoints);
            }
        }// end method paint
```

```
        private void btnReset_Click(object sender, EventArgs e)
        {
            // create a new arrayList
            aryPoints = new System.Collections.ArrayList();
            panel1.Invalidate( );
            // and make sure paint is called
        }
    }
}
```

This may need a short explanation. An ArrayList (aryPoints) and brush are created with the lines:

```
    System.Collections.ArrayList aryPoints = new
System.Collections.ArrayList();
```

When the mouse button is clicked, the mouse X and Y points are added to the dynamic arraylist (aryPoints). The X and Y position of the mouse is passed with the MouseEventArgs (e) and obtained from e.X and e.Y. The panel is invalidated, which causes it to be repainted by calling the panel's paint event.

The panel's paint event draws a filled polygon if there are more than 2 points. The FillPolygon method fills a polygon defined by an array of Points, so the ArrayList has to be converted to an array. This is done with the line of code:

```
 Point[ ] arrayofPoints = (Point[ ])aryPoints.ToArray(aryPoints[0].GetType( ));
```

The ArrayList can hold different types of data, so GetType is used to pass that information to the arrayofPoints array.

Finally when the Reset button is clicked a new ArrayList is created and the panel invalidated creating a new blank panel.

Your program should produce a display similar to figure 10.8 when the form is clicked:

Figure 10.8 Polygons

4. A Scribble program.

Write a program that draws a line which follows the mouse movement. Hint: you will have to use the mousemove event.

Summary

In this chapter we have seen how to draw graphics. We have seen how to use the pen and brush to draw lines and basic shapes such as ellipse and rectangle, as well as more complicated shapes such as arcs, pie and filled pie. We have seen how the Paint method works and how to override the Paint method to ensure our drawings are always redrawn. Finally we have seen how we can add multimedia controls to our programs.

11   Debugging

11.1   Introduction

Sooner or later your programs will have a problem that causes a run-time error, hangs the computer, or just fails to work. I expect that has already happened to you by now. You will need to debug the program to find out why it's not working. The development environment has tools to help you debug your program and get it working. It should be noted however that the debug features are different between the Express and Full versions.

The compiler will detect syntax errors and anything else it can't understand and it does go a long way to ensuring the program will remove many errors so that it will compile, but your program may still fail due to a run-time or logic error. Typical run-time errors are: divide by zero, text box type conversion error, or opening a non-existent file. We have seen how to trap run-time exceptions using try and catch code, but in this chapter we shall study how to use the debugger within the development environment.

11.2   Writing to the Debug Window

Before we start using the debugger, let's see how we can write a variable's value to the debug window using C# commands. We do this using the Debug.WriteLine method which is held in the System.Diagnostics namespace.

Start a new project and place a textbox and a button on the form. Set the text box's multiline property to true and add some text to the box (e.g. 'line 1', 'line 2' etc.). We shall display this in the debug output window.

Change the button click code to the following:

```
private void button1_Click(object sender, EventArgs e)
{
    // Create a string array and save the content of the lines.
    string[ ] tempArray = textBox1.Lines;

    // Loop through the array and write the array to the debug window.
    for (int count = 0; count < tempArray.Length; count++)
    {
        System.Diagnostics.Debug.WriteLine(tempArray[count]);
    }
}
```

Run the program. The following should appear in the debug window (see figure 11.1). If it the Output window isn't displayed, click Debug>Windows>Output.

```
Output                                                      ▾ ₽ X  1
Show output from:  Debug                    ▾ | 🔊 | 🔊 🔊 | ▤ | ⊡
  The thread 0x1f4 has exited with code 0 (0x0).
  'HelloWorld.vshost.exe' (Managed): Loaded 'C:\CSharp\HelloWorld\HelloWorld\bin\Debug\He
  'HelloWorld.vshost.exe' (Managed): Loaded 'C:\WINDOWS\assembly\GAC_MSIL\System.Configur
  line 1
  line 2
  line 3
```

Figure 11.1 The Debug Window Output

As well as adding code to display your variable's values in the Debug Window, you can also display them by using the development environment's debug features.

11.3   Using the Debugger

The debugger provides options to:

- Run the program to the cursor position or specified points (known as a breakpoint).
- To view, disable, enable and delete breakpoints.
- To set conditions on breakpoint operation.
- To pause the program.
- To restart in different ways after meeting a breakpoint or pause.
- To view, evaluate and modify variables.

11.3.1 Setting a breakpoint

If you want to run the program to a specific point, you can run to the cursor position or set a breakpoint. To run to the cursor, right-click the line you want to stop at and select 'run to cursor'. Alternatively, you can set as many breakpoints as you want by clicking the grey area to the left of the line of code where you want the breakpoint. A red circle is displayed and the line of code highlighted, see figure 11.2. The breakpoint is removed if the red circle is clicked a second time.

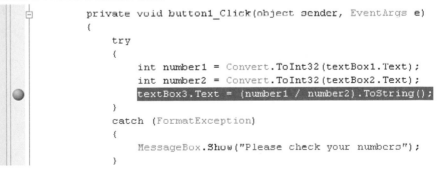

```csharp
private void button1_Click(object sender, EventArgs e)
{
    try
    {
        int number1 = Convert.ToInt32(textBox1.Text);
        int number2 = Convert.ToInt32(textBox2.Text);
        textBox3.Text = (number1 / number2).ToString();
    }
    catch (FormatException)
    {
        MessageBox.Show("Please check your numbers");
    }
```

Figure 11.2 Setting a breakpoint

The program will stop when it reaches the breakpoint and the line of code about to be executed is highlighted in yellow, with an arrow pointing it. If the cursor is now hovered over a variable its value will be displayed, see figure 11.3.

```
int number1 = Convert.ToInt32(textBox1.Text);
int number2 = Convert.ToInt32(textBox2.Text);
textBox3.Text = (number1 / number2).ToString();
// comment                        ◉ number2  123
```

Figure 11.3 Program stopped at breakpoint and displaying a value.

If the item is an object, you can also expand its detail ('drill down') by holding the cursor over the object and then moving to the plus symbol. Figure 11.4 shows the listBox object expanded to show the Items. You can see it has a count of 4 and the 'IsReadOnly' property is false. You could expand the non-public members further should you wish.

Figure 11.4 Displaying expanding object items

At this stage you can inspect variables, run the program at full speed (press the F5 key) or a line at a time (press F10 or F11). You can also change which line of code is to be executed next by dragging the yellow arrow to that line, but heed the warning! You can select these options from the debug toolbar, see figure 11.5. This appears when the program runs, but if it isn't displayed, choose View>Toolbars>Debug.

Figure 11.5. The Debug Toolbar

The toolbar icons from left to right are:
- start debugging (shortcut: F5)
- pause, or break all (ctrl + alt + break)

- stop debugging (shift + F5)
- restart, (ctrl + shift + F5)
- show next statement, (alt + Num *)
- step into, (F11)
- step over, (F10)
- step out, (shift + F11)
- toggle Hcx display and
- display the breakpoint windows (output, locals, watch, immediate and stack).

Breakpoints can be set before or at run-time, but they must be on executable code; you cannot set a breakpoint at a comment. You can switch them on and off with the F9 key. Remember, you can also disable and re-enable a breakpoint by right-clicking the red circle.

11.3.2 Pausing the Program

The program can be paused by using the pause button on the toolbar, when the line of code about to be executed will be displayed.

11.4 Conditional Breakpoints

If your breakpoint is in a loop, you may not want to break every time around the loop. With the full version of Visual studio, you can set breakpoints on a number of passes through a breakpoint, or when a variable has a certain value. You can set the conditions by right-clicking the red circle, see figure 11.6.

Figure 11.6 Breakpoint conditions

The conditions are:
- Location – when the program reaches a line and character location in a file (this doesn't have to be the current code file)
- Condition – the breakpoint is executed if the condition is true or has changed.
- Hit Count – the breakpoint is executed of the hit count is 1: always; 2: equal to, 3: multiple of, or 4: greater than or equal to
- Filter – you can filter out certain conditions, e.g. if thread or process ID = 12
- When hit – Print a message, or run a macro (mini program)

You can't do all of these with the Express edition, but you can add conditional or hit counts by adding extra code to do that for you, e.g.:

```
if ((loopCounter = 34) && (variable =123))
{
  count = count++;   // set breakpoint here
}
```

Remember, there has to be an executable line in the 'if' statement so that you can set a breakpoint. Adding this code will affect the timing of the loop, but that's unlikely to be a problem during debugging.

11.5   Restarting – Stepping code

To step the program a line at a time use 'Step Into' or 'Step Over'. Step Into steps the program a line at a time including any method calls. Step Over steps the program a line at a time, but runs any methods at full speed (unless they contain a breakpoint) and pauses at the line after the method call. You can also use Step Out, which takes you out of any methods you are debugging.

To use the Step Into, Step Over or Step Out commands press F11, F10 or Shift+F11, or click the icons on the debug toolbar, see figure 11.7

Figure 11.7 Restart option icons

11.6   The breakpoint windows

We have already seen the breakpoint output window where we can display variable values. The other windows you can select from the drop-down box are Local, Watch, Immediate and Call Stack.

11.6.1 Local window

This will display the local variables, see figure 11.8

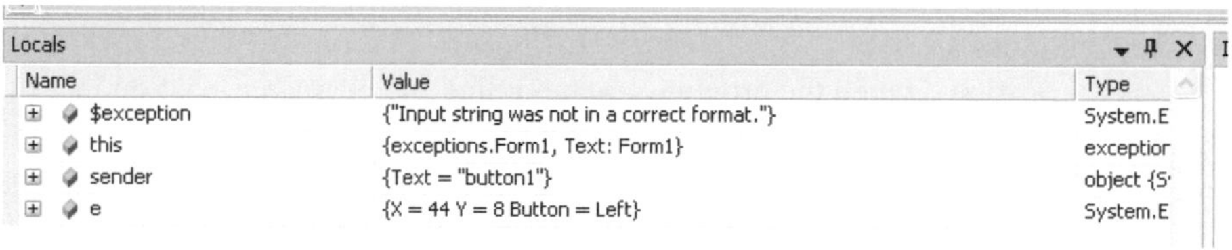

Locals		▾ ⏏ ✕
Name	Value	Type
⊞ ◈ $exception	{"Input string was not in a correct format."}	System.E
⊞ ◈ this	{exceptions.Form1, Text: Form1}	exceptior
⊞ ◈ sender	{Text = "button1"}	object {S'
⊞ ◈ e	{X = 44 Y = 8 Button = Left}	System.E

Figure 11.8 The Debug Local window

138

In this example the window is showing '$exception' - an exception message, 'this' - the current object (Text:Form1), 'sender' – the button that called the method (button1), and 'e' - the sender's arguments (in this case the mouse position X, Y and left-click).

11.6.2 Watch window

This is enabled when the program is at a breakpoint and is used to examine variables. The variables or expressions to be watched are set by entering them in the name field, see figure 11.9.

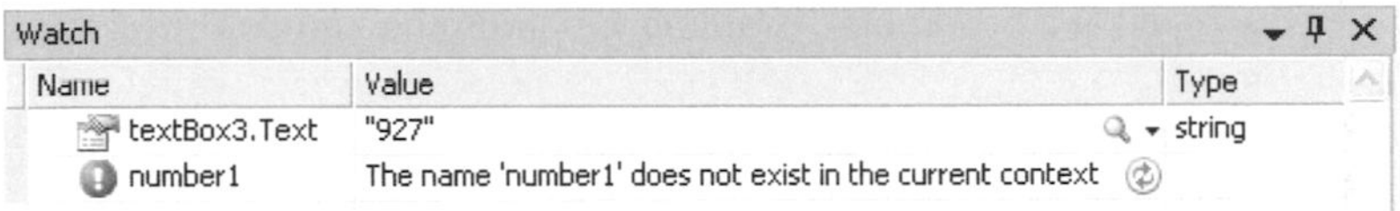

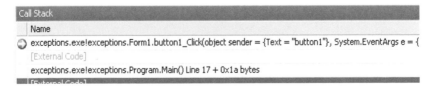

Figure 11.9 The Debug Watch window

In this example, textBox3.Text is being watched, and has the value 123. The other variable, number1, is not declared within this block of code, and so its value cannot be displayed.

11.6.3. The Immediate window.

This window lets you type in an expression to evaluate, see figure 11.10.

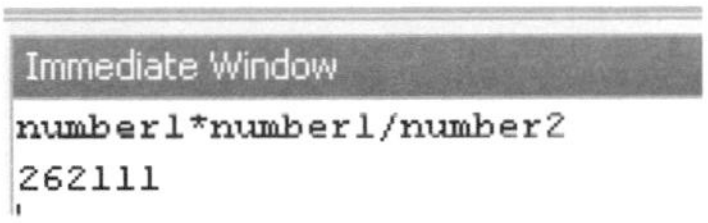

Figure 11.10 The Debug Immediate window

You can also use this window to assign values and then continue debugging.

11.6.4. The Call Stack.

This window lists the calls that were executed to get to the current code position. It can be useful to find out how your program got where it is. Figure 11.11 shows the current location came from a button click.

Figure 11.11 The Call Stack window

Self Assessment Exercises

You will get plenty of chances to debug your programs! But you might like to try some of the following:

1. Write to the debug window from your program.
2. Use the run to cursor command.
3. Set some breakpoints and run the program.
4. If your version supports it, try the breakpoint conditions.
5. Once stopped at a breakpoint, examine variables and know how to 'drill down into objects.
6. Step through your code using Step Into (F11), Step Over (F10) and Step Out (Shift+F11).
7. Use all the breakpoint windows.

Summary

We have covered how to use the debugger to correct your program errors. You can run the program to the cursor or a breakpoint. You can set, view, edit, enable and disable breakpoints. The debug windows help you view, evaluate and modify data and show the stack providing information on the calls that have been executed.

You can find out more on debugging by entering 'debugging [C#]' in the help search box.

12 Threading

12.1 Introduction

So far our programs have been running a single program or task at a time. You can split some programs into separate tasks called threads and run these tasks at the same time (concurrently) and for the threads to communicate with each other. Threading can speed up programs that use different resources such as files and networking, but at the same time may create resource sharing problems. As we will see in the next chapter we will use threads to perform networking tasks.

12.2 Threads

You can split your program into individual tasks, or threads. The .NET environment allows concurrent programming by controlling the execution of the threads.

Each thread is allocated a priority and runs either until it finishes, runs out of its allocated time, or is held up for some reason (e.g. waiting for some data, say from the internet or another thread). This operation is controlled by the operating system. You do not need a modern threading processor to run threaded programs.

Threads move between states. The thread states are:

- Unstarted – created, but waiting for Start
- Started – wait for Run
- Running – it runs when a processor is assigned to it (dispatched)
- Stopped – Thread is terminated or aborted
- Blocked – when making I/O request, waits for I/O
- WaitSleepJoin
    - Waiting for something else to happen (e.g. other code to complete)
    - Sleep for a specific time
    - Join (waiting for another thread to terminate)
- Suspend – a method call; goes to Started on Resume

The flow of a threaded program is shown in figure 12.1

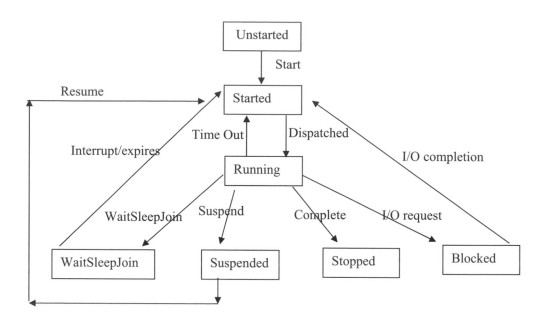

Figure 12.1 Thread states

12.3 Writing Thread Code

As you might expect the thread code is written as a class and a Thread object is instantiated the same way as any other object. Once a thread class is written, you can then instantiate and start as many threads as you want, just like you do with objects.

Threading code needs the System.Threading namespace (using System.Threading;) added to your code.

The thread code is in its own class, which can have its own methods. It is defined just like a class e.g.

```
Class MyThreadCode {
  // declarations
  public MyThreadCode ( )
    {
    // constructor
    }
  private myThreadMethods ( )
    {
    // methods go here
    }
} // end of thread code
```

The main code instantiates and starts the thread using ThreadStart as follows:

```
MyThreadCode myThread = new MyThreadCode();
Thread thread1 =
      new Thread (new ThreadStart ( MyThreadCode.StartMethod ));
```

ThreadStart is a delegate - an object that refers to a method and is used to call this method. It's like a pointer which allows a third-party program access to a method. We won't go into any more detail, just use the code provided.

The thread's properties can be accessed if necessary, e.g:

```
thread1.Name = "first Thread";
```

And then the thread can be started:

```
thread1.Start();
```

12.4   Thread sleeping example

Let's explain this with an example. Let's start by writing a thread that puts itself to sleep for a random amount of time and when it wakes up displays its name. We will later run as many of these threads as we want.

Start a new project and call it ThreadSleepExample.

Add a new class (Project > Add Class) and call it 'MySleepThread'

Add 'using System.Threading;' at the top of the thread class code, and type in the following code for the MySleepThread class:

```
namespace ThreadSleepExample
{
  class MySleepThread
  {
    // private declarations for each thread
    private int sleepTime;
    private static Random random = new Random( );

    // constructor

    public MySleepThread( )
    {
       sleepTime = random.Next(10000);      // random time to 10s
    }
```

```
    // Thread method
    // - displays name, sleeps and when woken, displays 'awake'
    public void MySleepMethod()
    {
        // get a reference to the current Thread
        Thread current = Thread.CurrentThread;
        // display message – sleeping for threadSleep time
        System.Diagnostics.Debug.WriteLine
                (current.Name + " sleeping for " + sleepTime);

        // Sleep
        Thread.Sleep(sleepTime);

        // Wake up ! - display message
        System.Diagnostics.Debug.WriteLine(current.Name + " awake !");
    }
    } // end ThreadCode
} // end namespace ThreadSleepExample
```

Note that the program writes to the console debug window, so this needs to be displayed if you want to see the output from the program. (Display with Debug > Windows > Output). If the program had used MessageBox.Show to display its output, the program would wait for input from the user, which isn't what we want.

As you can imagine, if there are multiple threads all trying to write to the same label or textbox to display their information, there can be a problem.

This thread needs to be instantiated and started. We shall do this when the form loads. Type the following code for the form load event:

```
    private void Form1_Load(object sender, EventArgs e)
    {
        MessageBox.Show("Starting thread");
        MySleepThread sleepThread = new MySleepThread();
        Thread thread1 = new Thread
            (new ThreadStart (sleepThread.MySleepMethod));
        thread1.Name = "first Thread";
        thread1.Start();    // and finally start the thread
    }
```

Run the program. The Debug output window will be similar to figure 12.2:

```
first Thread sleeping for 2292
The thread '<No Name>' (0xce0) has exited with code 0.
first Thread awake !
The thread '<No Name>' (0x684) has exited with code 0.
```
Figure 12.2 Thread output

12.5 Multiple Threading example

Now that we have some idea how threads start and run, let's expand the previous example to run multiple threads. We will simply change the form load code to create threads on a button click.

Repeat the above exercise. This time, instead of writing the form load code, add a button to the form. This time we will add a count to identify each thread. Add the following count declaration before 'public Form1 ( )' .

```
int count = 0;
```

Type the following code for the button click:

```
private void button1_Click(object sender, EventArgs e)
{
   count++;              // unique value for each thread
   MySleepThread sleepThread = new MySleepThread();
   Thread thread1 = new Thread
        (new ThreadStart(sleepThread.MySleepMethod));
   thread1.Name = "Thread " + count.ToString();
   thread1.Start();     // and finally start the thread
}
```

Run the program and click the button quickly a few times to run several threads. The output should be similar to figure 12.3:

```
Thread 1 sleeping for 3719
Thread 2 sleeping for 8907
Thread 3 sleeping for 1407
Thread 3 awake !
The thread 0xdac has exited with code 0.
Thread 1 awake !
The thread '<No Name>' (0xd64) has exited with code 0.
Thread 2 awake !
The thread '<No Name>' (0xd70) has exited with code 0.
```

Figure 12.3 Multiple thread output

Note that the threads run and sleep for different lengths of time. You have created a multi-tasking, concurrent program environment. We will not cover communication between threads here.

12.6 Accessing form controls from threads

You might get a situation where you want your thread to access a control such as a TextBox on a form. If you try to do this from a thread, you will get a 'cross-thread error' at run-time.

You cannot access an object owned by one thread from another thread. You program has to request that the owning thread do the work for you and to do so you call the control's invoke method (Control.Invoke) and pass it the data needed.

There are two ways to solve this problem.

1. In File Load event, add the code to ignore the error:

   CheckForIllegalCrossThreadCalls = false;

   But this isn't really good programming.

2. Provide the correct coding checks and call the Invoke method. We shall do this. If you really want to find out more about how Invoke works, you can refer to the Microsoft web site, or you can just do it!

Start a New Project and add a button and a TextBox on the form. Our thread will write to this text box.
Add the using statements and declare the count variable as before:

```
int count = 0;
```

For the button click add the following code:

```
private void button1_Click(object sender, EventArgs e)
{
    count++;
    // pass reference to this form
    MySleepThread sleepThread = new MySleepThread(this);
    Thread thread1 = new Thread
        (new ThreadStart(sleepThread.MySleepMethod));
    thread1.Name = "Thread " + count.ToString();
    thread1.Start();     // and finally start the thread
}
```

Note that this time we have used 'this' to pass a reference to the form from the thread.

We will now add the Invoke method so that we can write to the textbox from the thread.

Before public Form1 () add the delegate declaration.

delegate void SetTextCallBack(string text);

Add code to display on list box using cross threaded code, say before private void button1_Click:

```
public void WriteToTextBox(string strText)
{
    // InvokeRequired compares the thread ID of the
    // calling thread to the thread ID of the creating thread.
    // if different, it calls Invoke (when it will be the same).

    if (this.textBox1.InvokeRequired)
    {
        SetTextCallBack d = new SetTextCallBack(WriteToTextBox);
        this.Invoke(d, new Object[ ] { strText } );
    }
    else // it's OK  - add text to text box
    {
        this.textBox1.Text += strText;
    }
}  //end WriteToTextBox
```

Add a new Class (MySleepClass) and type the following code:

```
class MySleepThread
{
    // declarations
    private int sleepTime;
    private static Random random = new Random();
    private Form1 f;                    // Reference to Form1

    // constructor
    public MySleepThread(Form1 f)
    {
        sleepTime = random.Next(10000); // random time to 10 s
        this.f = f;                     // Assign a reference to form1
    }

    // Thread method
    public void MySleepMethod()
    {                                   // get reference to current Thread
        Thread current = Thread.CurrentThread;

        // Sleep
        Thread.Sleep(sleepTime);
```

```
        // Wake up ! - display message on text box

        f.WriteToTextBox(current.Name + " awake !\r\n");
        // f is reference to form1
    }
} // end ThreadCode
```

Run the program. The output should be similar to figure 12.4.

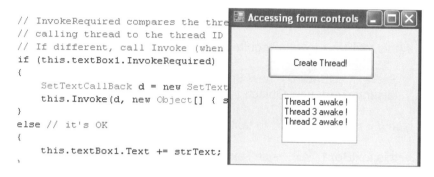

Figure 12.4 Accessing form controls

12.7   Other Thread considerations

We have only touched on threading here, for instance we haven't seen how to pass data between threads. Also there can be problems running threaded programs, not least of all that high priority threads can starve low priority ones, and threads may hang waiting on each other. This is without mentioning synchronisation, thread communication and using buffers, but we have covered the basics here. This will be enough for us to deal with internet communications in the next chapter.

Self Assessment Exercises

1. Change the code in 12.4 so that it uses MessageBox.Show() rather than write to the debug output window and see what happens.

2. Write Invoke code to write to other controls, say a listbox or label.

3. Find out more about delegates

4. Find out how to pass data and communicate between threads.

Summary

This has been a brief introduction to threaded programs. We have seen why we need threaded programs. We have seen the various states a thread can take and how they move from one state to another. We have seen how to write a threaded program and how to put them to sleep. We have run a multi-threaded program, each of which can access the same form control to report its progress. We have also mentioned possible problems with threaded programs. All of this provides the background for internet communications that we will cover next.

13 Internet Applications

13.1 Introduction

Now that we have some idea about how we use threads to run sections of our program concurrently, we can see how to apply that to an internet application. In this chapter we will write internet communication programs using threads that will wait for data to be received from the internet and at the same time be able to send data to the internet. Without threads the programs would hang waiting for data to be received. We shall look at programs using the internet communication protocols Transmission Control Protocol (TCP) and User Datagram Protocol (UDP). We will end up with an internet chat program.

13.2 Client-Server communication

We will start by looking at client-server internet communication. In this case the client (e.g. a user typing a web request) sends a request to a server which responds with the data. This response could be an HTML page, a file transfer, an ASP.NET page request or many other items. Initially we will look at a TCP server application that receives data and then expand this to respond with data. We will then study a TCP client application which sends data and finally to display the server's response. Having produced this TCP communication program, we will write a similar program using UDP protocols.

Networking capabilities are provided through the System.Net.Sockets namespace. There are no controls to be placed on the form. The communication sockets are created at run-time.

13.3 TCP and UDP

The two main protocols used by the internet are TCP (Transmission Control Protocol) and UDP (User Datagram Protocol). The main difference is that TCP implements a connection and re-transmissions whereas the UDP protocol just sends data in packets and doesn't care if they are received. UDP is useful in streaming technology when re-transmission is irrelevant.

TCP communication is based on streaming (similar to streaming we saw with disk I/O). A process or program establishes a connection to another process and data transfers occur in continuous streams. The alternative UDP communication uses packet based transmissions known as datagram sockets. This protocol is a connectionless service in which packets are sent and can arrive in any order. This requires more programming, but may result in a faster performance.

We shall start with TCP communications and as our server will wait for connections and client requests we will use threads. If you are unsure about these read the chapter on threads again.

13.4 Creating a TCP server.

A TCP server simply listens on the internet at a port and at the computer's IP address. There are five steps to creating a TCP streaming server:

1. Create a server using a TCPListener with the code which sets up the IP and port addresses. A TCPListener object is created with the following code:

   ```
   Int32 port = 5000;
   IPAddress localAddr = IPAddress.Parse("127.0.0.1");
   TcpListener server = new TcpListener(localAddr, port);
   ```

   The program 'listens' at the port number and the computer's IP (Internet Protocol) address. Port values below 1204 are reserved. The IP address 127.0.0.1 or "localhost" refers to the host computer, so you can run the client and server applications on any PC and you don't need to know or change the IP address for different PCs.

2. Start listening at the port. The TcpListener we called 'server' is started with the command:

   ```
   server.Start( );
   ```

   The server simply listens at this address. The server creates a connection to the client when a client request is received via a socket.

3. Establish the connection between client and server. To start the TCPListener, use the code:

   ```
   Socket connection= server.AcceptSocket( );
   ```

   Socket is in the System.Net.Sockets namespace, so at the top of your code, you will need to add:

   ```
   using System.Net.Sockets;
   ```

4. Communicate with the client. Create the network stream and use the Socket methods Send( ) and Receive( ). We also create BinaryReader and BinaryWriter, read and write objects. By contrast the UDP communications use SendTo( ) and ReceiveFrom( ) methods.

5. Terminate the connection. Use the Socket method Close( ).

13.5 Threads

As we have said without threads, the program would hang waiting for data to be received. We will put the Receive method into a thread allowing other sections of our program to run; the thread will continue when data is received. We shall see how this all works in the following example. Remember if we want to write to a textbox or other control from a thread we will have to deal with cross-thread exceptions.

13.6   Creating a TCP client

The TcpClient makes the connection to the server at the PCs port and IP address. Four steps have to be taken to create a TCP client:

1. Create a TcpClient client and connect to the server using the code:

   ```
   TcpClient client = new TcpClient();
   Client.connect (serverAddress, serverPort);
   ```

The Client code will connect to a server, so the **serverAddress** is either the IP address of the server of type 'IPAddress' (e.g. 127.0.0.1, see above) or a string containing its name (e.g. "localhost"). The **serverPort** is the port number of the server, i.e. the one we used when we created the server. To run code on your PC, use the local IP address 127.0.0.1 or "localhost", otherwise you will need to know the IP address of your computer. You can find this in Control Panel or you can run the MSDOS command 'ipconfig'. It's a number like 192.123.456.7.

2. Create the network stream using the **TcpClient getStream( )** method.
3. Communicate with the server using the NetworkStream methods **Read( )**, **ReadByte( )**, **Write( )** or **WriteByte( )**.
4. Finally close the connection using the method **Close( )**.

13.7   TCP Client-Server application

We shall develop a program with a TCP server that receives and echoes data sent to it and then add a TCP client that sends data to the server and displays the data returned. We could extend this so the server does some useful work such as squaring any numbers sent to it, or retrieving data from a file.

Start a new application and call it Server. On the form place a list box (called lstRxdData) and buttons to listen and disconnect (btnListen and btnDisconnect). Your GUI should look similar to Figure 13.1.

Figure 13.1. Server application

At the following to the using statements at the top of the code:

```
using System.Net.Sockets;
using System.Net;
using System.IO;
using System.Threading;   // we'll need threads later
```

Before the code public Form () add the declarations:

```
private Socket connection;
private NetworkStream socketStream;
private BinaryReader reader;
private BinaryWriter writer;
```

Add the following method:

```
public void RunServer()
{
    try          //    and catch (Exception error)
    {
      // create listener
      Int32 port = 5000;
      IPAddress localAddr = IPAddress.Parse("127.0.0.1");
      TcpListener server = new TcpListener(localAddr, port);
        // defined in System.Net.Sockets

      server.Start( );        // start listening

      // establish and accept connection
      connection = server.AcceptSocket( );

      // Create a NetworkStream for the socket
      socketStream = new NetworkStream(connection);
```

```csharp
//create read and write objects to send data through stream
writer = new BinaryWriter(socketStream);
reader = new BinaryReader(socketStream);

// display on listBox this will cross thread error
lstRxdData.Items.Add("connection made");

// and tell client
writer.Write("Message from Server: connected OK");

// now loop reading and displaying data received

string msgFromClient = null;
do
{
  try
    {

    // read the string sent by client and terminate if QUIT
    msgFromClient = reader.ReadString();

    lstRxdData.Items.Add(msgFromClient);
    // won't hang because it'll be in a thread

   // and echo data
     writer.Write(msgFromClient);

   } // end try
     catch (Exception)
   {
     break;
   } // catch
}
while (msgFromClient != "QUIT");     // close if QUIT received

lstRxdData.Items.Add("Client disconnected");

// and close connection
reader.Close();
writer.Close();
socketStream.Close();
connection.Close();
} // end try
catch (Exception error)
{
  MessageBox.Show(error.ToString());
```

```
    } // catch

  } // end RunServer
```

RunServer will be run as a thread.

For the listen button click we are going to instantiate and start the RunServer thread code:

1. If it isn't present, add the using statement: using System.Threading;
2. Add the private declaration: private Thread serverThread;
3. Change the code for the listen button click to:

```
private void btnListen_Click(object sender, EventArgs e)
{
   serverThread = new Thread(new ThreadStart(RunServer));
   serverThread.Start();
   btnListen.Enabled = false;
}
```

Add the code for disconnect button:

```
private void btnDisconnect_Click(object sender, EventArgs e)
{
   try
   {
      if (connection.Connected)
      {
         reader.Close();
         writer.Close();
         socketStream.Close();
         connection.Close();
         btnDisconnect.Enabled = false;
      }
   } // try
   catch (Exception error)
   {
      MessageBox.Show(error.ToString());
   } // catch
}
```

.NET security won't let a thread write directly to a control on the form, (you get illegal cross thread error) so to make life easy, add this line to the Form_load( ) event:

```
CheckForIllegalCrossThreadCalls = false;
```

If you want to do it the correct way, see the chapter on threads and use the Invoke method.

Check the code runs. You will get an error on disconnecting because a connection hasn't been made by a client. Save and close the project. We now create a TCP client that sends data to the server.

13.8   TCP Client Code

We will now create a second application which will act as a TCP client. Both this and the TCP server can be tested on the same PC.

1. Create a form as before with listbox (lstRxdData) and buttons (btnConnect and btnDisconnect), this time call the button 'Connect, rather than 'Listen'
    Now add a textbox (txtSendData).

    The design should be similar to figure 13.2

2. Add the using statements as before (IO, Net, Net.Sockets and Threading)
3. Add the private declarations as follows:

    ```
    private NetworkStream clientStream;
    private BinaryReader reader;
    private BinaryWriter writer;
    private Thread clientThread;
    private string message = null;
    ```

4. Now add the client code and thread code:

    ```
    public void RunClient()
    {
      TcpClient client;
      // init tcpClient
      try
      {
        // 1. Create client and connect to server- give
        client = new TcpClient();

        // give IP address and port to talk to
        client.Connect("localhost", 5000);

        // get network stream
        clientStream = client.GetStream();

        // create read and write objects
        writer = new BinaryWriter(clientStream);
    ```

```
        reader = new BinaryReader(clientStream);
        lstRxdData.Items.Add("connecting to server");

    // we will ignore cross-thread errors in form load,

        do
          try
          {
            // read message from server until QUIT received
            message = reader.ReadString();
            lstRxdData.Items.Add(message);
          } // try
          catch (Exception error)
          {
            MessageBox.Show("Error reading from server "+error.ToString());
          } // catch
        while (message != "QUIT");
      // close connection
      lstRxdData.Items.Add("Closing connection");
      writer.Close();
      reader.Close();
      clientStream.Close();
      client.Close();
      btnConnect.Enabled = true;        // re-enable connct button

      } // end try
      catch (Exception error)
      {
        MessageBox.Show("Error creating connection " + error.ToString());
      }

    } // end runclient
```

5. To start the thread when the connect button is clicked, change the button click code to following:

```
    private void btnConnect_Click(object sender, EventArgs e)
    {
      clientThread = new Thread(new ThreadStart(RunClient));
      clientThread.Start()
      btnConnect.Enabled = false;
    }
```

6. Ignore cross-thread errors. Add this line to the Form_load( ) event:

```
    CheckForIllegalCrossThreadCalls = false;
```

7. Finally add the code for the KeyDown event to send data when enter is pressed in text box:

```
private void txtSendData_KeyDown(object sender, KeyEventArgs e)
{
    if (e.KeyCode == Keys.Enter)
    {
        // when enter key pressed, write to writer (binaryWriter to ClientStream)
        writer.Write(txtSendData.Text);
        // and clear text box
        txtSendData.Clear();
    }
}
```

Run this client code from the Visual Studio environment and the previous server .EXE code from its bin>Debug folder.

Press Listen to start the server listening and press Connect on the Client. You may be trapped out by your firewall, but the server should display the message 'connection made' and the client the message: 'connecting to server' and 'Message from Server: connected OK'

You can now type messages in the client and they are echoed back. Your program displays should be similar to figure 13.2.

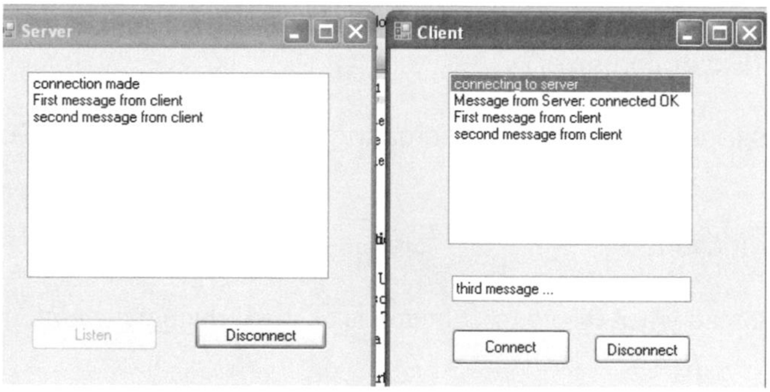

Figure 13.2 TCP Client and Server displays

You can type QUIT to close the programs

13.9   UDP communications – A chat program

Let's now design a communication (chat) program using the UDP protocols. This time we will use the UDPClient class which both sends and receives; there is no Server or Listener class. This is different from the TCP protocol we saw which had individual

Server and Client applications. We will design one program that both sends and receives and run two versions of this program that will chat to each other.

We shall use the UdpClient's Send and Receive methods to send and receive data. We will then run a second copy of this program to chat. We don't have to make a connection; the program will just send or receive data to an IPaddress and port.

13.9.1 UDPClient.Send( )

The Send method sends a datagram packet. Its parameters are: a UDP datagram byte array, the number of bytes to be sent, the destination host name and port address.

The datagram packet to be sent is a byte array created from a string using System.Text.Encoding's GetBytes method:

```
byte[ ] sendData = System.Text.Encoding.ASCII.GetBytes(string);
```

This will be sent to the server using the code:

```
client.Send(sendData, sendData.Length, "IPaddress", int.Parse("port"));
```

'IPaddress' and 'port' are the IP address and port of the destination computer.

13.9.2 UDPClient.Receive( )

The UDPClient.Receive method accepts a datagram packet. Our program will be put in a loop waiting to receive data and this is put in a thread so our program won't hang waiting for data. The Receive method has one parameter, an IPEndpoint. The IPEndpoint is a combined IP address and port number of the remote host from which the data was sent. We can use this to send the data received back to the client using the Send method.

The Receive method returns the datagram packet received as a byte array. We shall use the following code to accept the data:

```
byte[ ] rxdata = client.Receive(ref this.rxPoint);
```

Note that the 'ref' keyword is used and rxPoint is updated by the Receive method with the sender's IP and port, so we know where to respond. We will use rxPoint in the Send method.

13.9.3 UDP program threads

Let's try our UDP chat program. We will start with just one application which uses only UDPClient classes to both send and receive; I will call them 'client' and 'server'. The client will send data typed into a textbox to the server, the server will display this data and reply echoing the data back to the client. As both the server and client will have to wait for data there will be two threads, we'll call them WaitForDataFromClient and WaitForDataFromServer.

Initially we will run the application on our PC using 'localhost', but later we will run a second version of the program so a true chat will run. It could then be run on separate PCs, so long as the IP addresses are known.

The communication will be set up as shown in figure 13.3.

Rather than ignoring IllegalCrossThread errors as we did previously, we shall correctly write from the threads to the list box display.

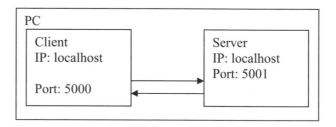

Figure 13.3 UDP Client - Server communications

13.9.4 UDP GUI design

Start a new project (UDPChat) and place a list box (lstRxdData) and a text box (txtData) on the form. The list box will display the data received. The text box will contain the data to be sent when the return key is pressed.

The IP and port values are declared at the start of the program. Port values less than 1024 are reserved; we will use 5000 and 5001.

Your interface should be similar to figure 13.4

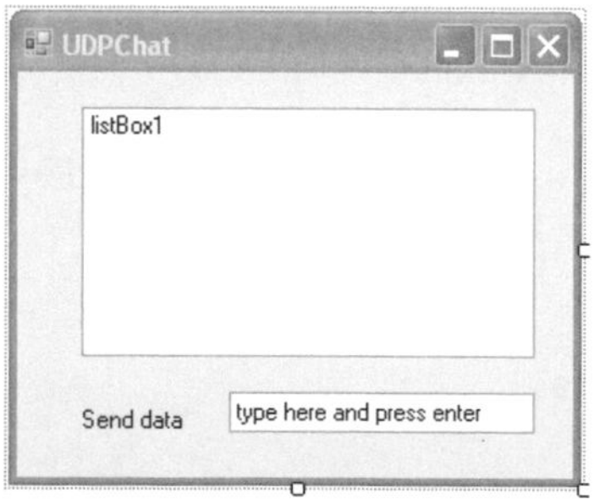

Figure 13.4 UDP Chat application

We will start by writing the server thread code that waits for data from the client using the UDPClient.Receive method.

13.9.5 UDP server code

Add the following at the top of your code:

```
using System.Net;
using System.Net.Sockets;
using System.Threading;
```

We have to declare a UdpClient which be the server and create and start a thread which waits for data from the client and puts this in the list box.

Declare an UdpClient and an IPEndPoint for the server. Add the following code after the declaration: public partial class Form1 : Form {

```
// Server
UdpClient server = new UdpClient(5001);
IPEndPoint rxPoint = new IPEndPoint(new IPAddress(0), 0);

// add the thread call to allow us to write to the list box as well:
delegate void SetTextCallBack(string text);
```

Follow this with the method that waits for the data from the client:

```
// Server code
private void WaitForDataFromClient ()
{
    while (true)
    {
        // receive data from server
        byte[ ] ClientData = server.Receive(ref rxPoint);

        // display on list box
        ListBoxDisplay("Server received: " +
            (System.Text.Encoding.ASCII.GetString(ClientData)));

        // and echo back
        ListBoxDisplay("Sending back");
        server.Send(ClientData, ClientData.Length, rxPoint);
    } // end while true
} // end WaitForDataFromClient
```

To write to the list box from the thread add the following code after the code you have just entered:

```
private void ListBoxDisplay(string message)
```

```
    {
        this.SetListBox(message);
    }

    private void SetListBox(string strText)
    {
      if (this.lstRxdData.InvokeRequired)
      {
        SetTextCallBack d = new SetTextCallBack(SetListBox);
        this.Invoke(d, new Object[ ]{strText});
      }
      else // it's OK
      {
        this.lstRxdData.Items.Add(strText);
      }
    }          //end SetListBox
```

Now we need to start the server's thread.
Add the following after InitializeComponent( );

```
        // start server
        Thread serverThread = new Thread
            (new ThreadStart(WaitForDataFromClient));
        serverThread.Start();
```

You can now run the program to check it. You may have to give your firewall access to your program.

Now we need to declare the UdpClient 'client' and use the Send method to send the data.

Add the following code to declare the 'client' and endpoint after the 'UdpClient server' declaration:

```
        UdpClient client = new UdpClient(5000);
        IPEndPoint txPoint = new IPEndPoint(new IPAddress(0), 0);
```

Change the KeyDown event for the text box to the following:

```
    private void txtData_KeyDown(object sender, KeyEventArgs e)
    {
      if (e.KeyCode == Keys.Enter)
      {
        // create a string datagram packet
        string packet = txtData.Text;

        // convert packet to byte array
```

```
        byte[ ] sendData = System.Text.Encoding.ASCII.GetBytes(packet);

        // send to server on port defined in remote port text box
        this.client.Send(sendData, sendData.Length, "localhost", 5001);
        // and clear text box
        txtData.Clear();
    }
}
```

Check the program runs. Your firewall may block your program, but you should be able to type into the text box and see the message 'Server received:' followed by the message in the list box.

The thread that was started continues when you close the window. You will have to stop debugging to add further code.

Note that although the server code echoes the data using server.Send(ClientData, ClientData.Length, rxPoint); and it's not received by the client, we don't get an error message. We'll write the code to accept the data now.

13.9.6 UDP client code

Now we have to add the client code to accept the data echoed from the 'server'. This will be put in a thread. We have already declared the UDPClient object and transmit IPEndPoint for the client.

Add the thread code to wait for data sent by the server. This will echo the data sent by the server.

Add the following after the WaitForDataFromClient method:

```
private void WaitForDataFromServer()
{
    while (true)
    {
        // receive data from client
        byte[ ] rxdata = client.Receive(ref this.txPoint);
        // cross-thread exception if lstRxdData.Items.Add ( ) is used
        // so call
        ListBoxDisplay("Client received: " +
            System.Text.Encoding.ASCII.GetString(rxdata));
    }
}// end of wait for data
```

Declare and start the thread 'WaitForDataFromServer' which waits for data. Add the following code after InitializeComponent( );

```
Thread clientThread = new Thread(new
        ThreadStart(WaitForDataFromServer));
clientThread.Start( );
```

You can now run the program, data typed into the text box is sent to the 'server', echoed back and displayed by the 'client' on the list box, see figure 13.5

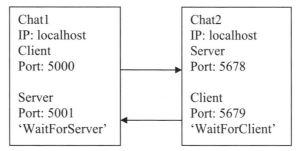

Figure 13.5 UDPChat Display

13.10 A Local Chat program

We can now try to run our program as a true chat program. We will run two copies of our chat program on the same PC. To do this we have to use 2 different ports. We can't run the same program twice, as they will both try to use the same port and an error would occur. They will communicate as shown in figure 13.6.

```
Chat1                      Chat2
IP: localhost              IP: localhost
Client                     Server
Port: 5000      ────────▶  Port: 5678

Server                     Client
Port: 5001      ◀────────  Port: 5679
'WaitForServer'            'WaitForClient'
```

Figure 13.6 Remote chat program communications

We will make a copy of our first program (Chat2), and change the port addresses for this to 5678 and 5679. We will also change the port address to which Chat1 writes to 5678.

Return to the chat program and change the following line from:

        this.client.Send(sendData, sendData.Length, "localhost", 5001);
to:

164

```
this.client.Scnd(scndData, sendData.Length, "localhost", 5678);
```

At this point, it's easiest to run a second Visual Studio application. Make a copy of the folder containing your project and open this in the second VS application. Change the server and client declarations for the second program as follows:

From: UdpClient server = new UdpClient(5001);
to:

                   UdpClient server = new UdpClient(5678);

and from: UdpClient client = new UdpClient(5000);
to:

                   UdpClient client = new UdpClient(5679);

Make sure the KeyDown event now sends to port 5001, as originally:

```
this.client.Send(sendData, sendData.Length, "localhost", 5001);
```

compile and run both programs (or run the EXE files) and chat, see figure 13.7

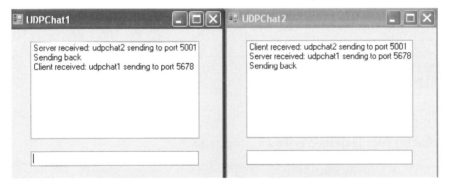

Figure 13.7

13.11 Remote Chat program

You can now try to the run the programs on separate PCs, as shown in figure 13.8.

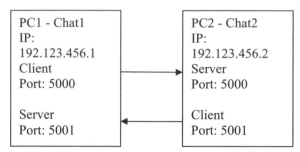

Figure 13.8 Remote chat IP and port connections

You will have to find out your IP addresses and change the code, for example:

this.client.Send(sendData, sendData.Length, "192.168.1.104", 5001);

You will also have to check your port addresses.

I had the following IP and port addresses

	PC	Laptop
IP:	IP: 192.168.1.104	IP: 192.168.1.100
KeyDown sends to IP & port	192.168.1.100, 5678	192.168.1.104, 5001
Server port	5001	5678
Client port	5000	5679

The port to reply to is obtained from rxPoint in the **server.Receive(ref rxPoint)**; code.

The resulting communication is shown in figure 13.9.

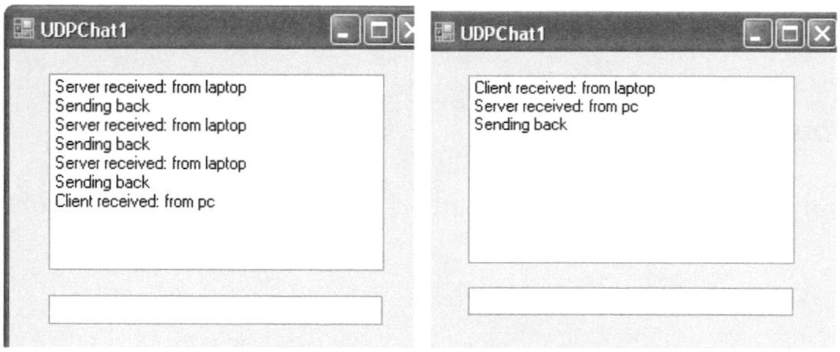

Figure 13.9 PC and Laptop displays

13.12 Finding your PC's IP address:

The following code will display your PC's name and IP address:

You need to add 'using System.Net;'

```
string hostName = Dns.GetHostName();
MessageBox.Show ("Host Name = " + hostName);
IPHostEntry local = Dns.GetHostEntry(hostName);
foreach (IPAddress ipaddress in local.AddressList)
  {
MessageBox.Show("IPAddress = " + ipaddress.ToString());
  }
```

Self Assessment Exercises

1. TCP Server:

Having created the first TCP client and server applications, make the server to do a useful task such as square a number sent to it. You will need to think about the data string you receive, how to check that it is a number and how to reply with either the square of the number or an error message.

2. Change the TCP server and client code so that it reads the IP and port address from text boxes.

Basically, the TcpListener will be instantiated as follows:

```
TcpListener server = new TcpListener
        (IPAddress.Parse(txtIp.Text), int.Parse(txtListenerPort.Text););
```

Change the client connect code to:

```
client.Connect(txtIP.Text, int.Parse(txtServerPort.Text));
```

3. Change UDP code so that it reads the IP and port address from text boxes.

You will have to read the port values before instantiating the server and client UdpClient objects and then start the 'serverThread' and 'clientThread' threads.

The Client.Send method should send to the IP address entered into a text box.

Remember the port values are integers, whereas the IP address is a string

4. Expand this to the remote chat program, so that one program only needs to be used for can be used

Summary

In this chapter we have seen the TCP and UDP communications and programs. The TCP program uses separate TCPListener and TCPClient objects and a server which listens on the internet and a client which connects to the server. The code is put into threads and the communication uses Read and Write methods. The UDP application uses UDPClient objects only and connectionless communication using Send and Receive methods.

Both TCP and UDP communication chat programs were developed. The UDP program initially started with a single application that communicated via the internet and 'localhost'. This was extended to two separate applications which communicated on the same PC, and then extended further to communicate across the internet to any internet address.

14   Introduction to Databases

14.1   Introduction

Databases themselves are a vast subject. The following few chapters intend to give you a feel for databases, how to display the data in a database, how to create your own databases and access database data from code.

A database is an integrated collection of data. The most popular database systems are relational databases which consist of separate but linked tables of data. In this way an item of data is held in only one place. Databases are often manipulated and queried using a language called SQL (structured query language). There are also .NET extensions that enable query and other operations, called LINQ (Language-Integrated Query), but we shall not look at these.

In this chapter we will firstly view data in an existing database and secondly create our own database. In the next chapter we will see how to display this data on a GUI and then finally access this database using code. To perform these tasks, you must have installed the Visual Studio Database option. If not, do so now.

14.2   A typical database

Before we start let's look at a typical database.

As we said, a relational database is composed of different tables. Microsoft's Northwind database example is a typical database that might be used by a company and has tables for customers, orders, products, suppliers, etc., all of which are linked together. Figure 14.1 shows a portion of the employees table, which shows the table's rows (the individual employee's data) and columns (or fields: Last Name, First Name etc).

		Last Name	First Name	Title	Title C	Birth Date	Hire Date	Address	City	Region
+	1	Davolio	Nancy	Sales Representative	Ms	08-Dec-1968	01-May-1992	507 - 20th Ave. E.	Seattle	WA
+	2	Fuller	Andrew	Vice President, Sales	Dr.	19-Feb-1952	14-Aug-1992	908 W. Capital Way	Tacoma	WA
+	3	Leverling	Janet	Sales Representative	Ms	30-Aug-1963	01-Apr-1992	722 Moss Bay Blvd.	Kirkland	WA
+	4	Peacock	Margaret	Sales Representative	Mrs	19-Sep-1958	03-May-1993	4110 Old Redmond Rd.	Redmond	WA
+	5	Buchanan	Steven	Sales Manager	Mr.	04-Mar-1955	17-Oct-1993	14 Garrett Hill	London	
+	6	Suyama	Michael	Sales Representative	Mr.	02-Jul-1963	17-Oct-1993	Coventry House	London	
+	7	King	Robert	Sales Representative	Mr.	29-May-1960	02-Jan-1994	Edgeham Hollow	London	
+	8	Callahan	Laura	Inside Sales Coordinator	Ms	09-Jan-1958	05-Mar-1994	4726 - 11th Ave. N.E.	Seattle	WA
+	9	Dodsworth	Anne	Sales Representative	Ms	02-Jul-1969	15-Nov-1994	7 Houndstooth Rd.	London	

Figure 14.1 The Northwind Database

You may already have the Microsoft Access Northwind database on your PC but it can be downloaded from the Microsoft web site.

A particular row of a table is called a record and consists of fields, or columns, of data. To link tables, there must be a unique item in each record known as the primary key field; in this case it is the employee's ID. Other columns may have duplicate data though, for example one employee's first name, date of birth or department may be the same as another employee.

Structured Query Language (SQL) provides a set of commands that enable programmers to define complex queries to select data from a database. It enables users to extract different information from the database. For instance one user might want to know the names of all the employees working in a department but another user, employees over the age of 60, or paid a certain salary. We will look at the basic SQL commands later, but won't get involved in extracting specific data.

14.3   Dealing with Databases

We shall look at the following in this chapter:

1. Inspect and view data in an existing database
2. Creating our own database

In the following chapters we shall see how to use the GUI controls to display data and finally how to access database from code.

14.3.1 Viewing a database in C#

We will start by creating an application that will simply view the Microsoft Access database Northwind. You may already have this in your PC, if not you can download it from Microsoft. It's a complicated URL so to find it, perform an internet search for 'Northwind database'. Alternatively, you can move on to the section 14.4 on creating your own database and then return to this stage.

There are a few differences between the Express and Full editions. In the Express edition, the database explorer window is called Database Explorer, but in the Full edition it is called Solution Explorer.

Start a new windows application and call it 'ViewingADb'. To view and add a database to the project, display either the Database Explorer or Server Explorer, depending on the version of Visual Studio you have. To display this window select either View > Server Explorer or View > Other Windows > Database Explorer. This displays a window which has a section called Data Connections.

We will add a connection here to the Northwind database (or other database if you have one). Figure 14.2 shows the Data Connections and the Northwind database tables within both the Database Explorer and Server Explorer.

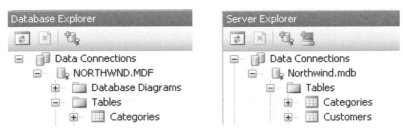

Figure 14.2 Database Explorer and Server Explorer windows

Add the connection from your program to the database. Right-click 'Data Connections' and choose 'Add Connection'. The Northwind Access database has a .MDB extension so select this for the data source and browse for the database. (If you have downloaded Northwind from the Microsoft site, it may be an SQL server database file, with an 'MDF' extension, so select that instead). There is no security on this database, so clear the username and password fields. See figure 14.3.

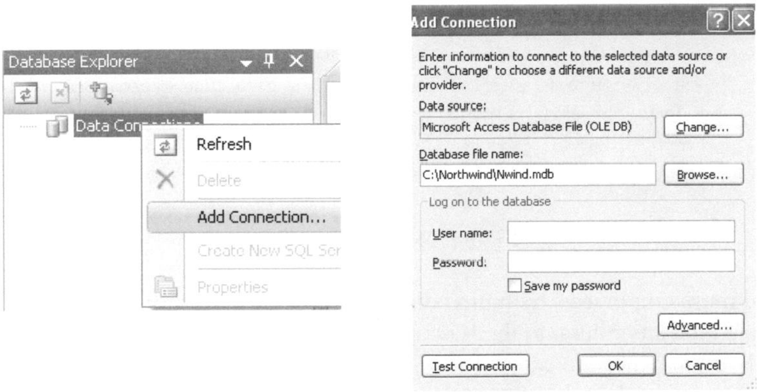

Figure 14.3 Adding a database connection

At this stage you can test the connection works. Click OK to add the database. It should appear in the Database/Server Explorer window as shown in figure 14.2

You may see different database files: Access database files which have an MDB file extension, SQL Server compact 3.5 database files which have an SDF extension and SQL Server database files which have a MDF file extension. There are others too, such as Oracle database files. The following instructions may vary slightly depending upon which database file you have chosen.

You can now expand the Northwind database in the Explorer, see figure 14.4. There are a number of Tables and Views. Expand the 'Tables' to see all the individual tables that make up the database.

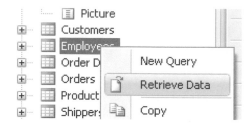

Figure 14.4 Database retrieving data

We can inspect, add or delete the data in the tables by right-clicking the table name in the explorer and selecting 'Retrieve Data'.

If you do this for the Employees table, you will see data similar to figure 14.5.

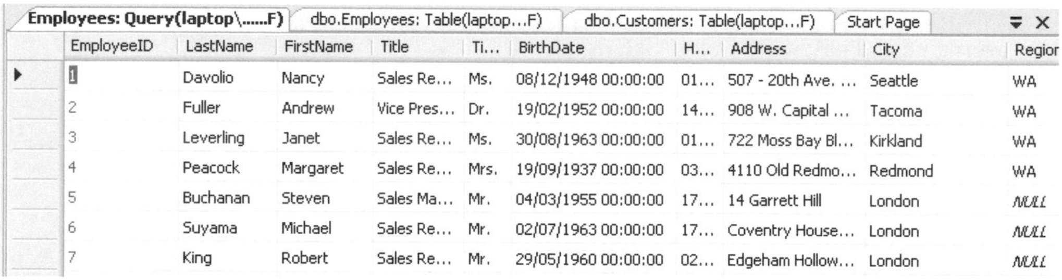

EmployeeID	LastName	FirstName	Title	Ti...	BirthDate	H...	Address	City	Region
1	Davolio	Nancy	Sales Re...	Ms.	08/12/1948 00:00:00	01...	507 - 20th Ave. ...	Seattle	WA
2	Fuller	Andrew	Vice Pres...	Dr.	19/02/1952 00:00:00	14...	908 W. Capital ...	Tacoma	WA
3	Leverling	Janet	Sales Re...	Ms.	30/08/1963 00:00:00	01...	722 Moss Bay Bl...	Kirkland	WA
4	Peacock	Margaret	Sales Re...	Mrs.	19/09/1937 00:00:00	03...	4110 Old Redmo...	Redmond	WA
5	Buchanan	Steven	Sales Ma...	Mr.	04/03/1955 00:00:00	17...	14 Garrett Hill	London	NULL
6	Suyama	Michael	Sales Re...	Mr.	02/07/1963 00:00:00	17...	Coventry House...	London	NULL
7	King	Robert	Sales Re...	Mr.	29/05/1960 00:00:00	02...	Edgeham Hollow...	London	NULL

Tabs: Employees: Query(laptop\......F) — dbo.Employees: Table(laptop...F) — dbo.Customers: Table(laptop...F) — Start Page

Figure 14.5 Table Data

You can add more employees, by typing directly into the cells. You must obey the data type and can't type anything into the ID column – this is generated automatically for you. Try this, but you may need to execute the SQL command to update the database, see figure 14.6. You can delete the row, but note that if you now add more employees, the ID you deleted isn't used again.

Figure 14.6 Execute SQL update

14.4   Creating a new database

As an example of creating a database, let's create our own DVD/MP3 record collection database. It will have two tables, called Artist and Recording. We will provide a link from the recording to the artist so that on adding a new recording, the user will have to select an artist from the Artist table.

Start a new project and call it CreatingAdB.

To add a new database select Project > Add New Item > Server-based Database, see figure 14.7. It's an MDF file. Give it a suitable name (e.g. 'Recordings') and add the database.

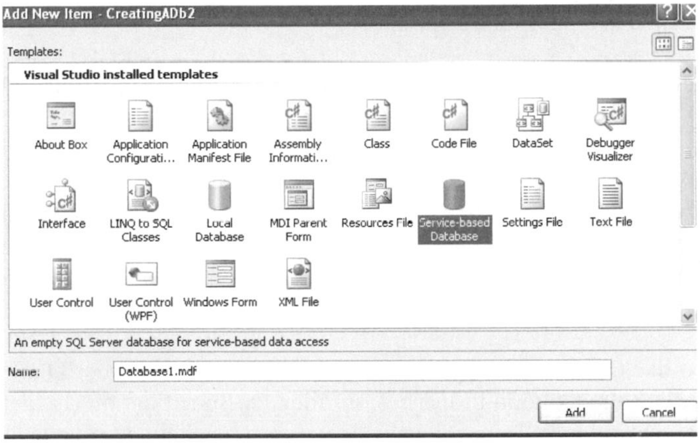

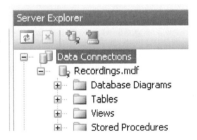

Figure 14.7 Adding an SQL database

Cancel the Data Source configuration dialog that appears. We will define the items in the database later. The database connection has been made and appears in the Database/Server Explorer, see figure 14.8.

Figure 14.8 Adding a database

To display Database/Server Explorer, you can double-click the database name in the Solution Explorer or use Views > Database / Server Explorer as you did in 14.3.1.

As we have seen, if you already have a database you can right-click Data Connections in Database/Server Explorer and browse for the database.

We will now add the tables which make up our database. If you find you don't have all the correct icons, check you have selected and MDF database and not an SDF database.

Let's add our tables. Right-click Tables in the Explorer and select Add New Table. We can now add the names and data types for each column of our database.

Let's create a database for our record collection. We will create tables for artist and recording, but we could also add group/solo artist, date, playing time, genre, record label etc. At a later date we could search for (say) a solo rock and roll artist, dated before 1980 whose playing time is longer than 3 minutes.

The first table we are going to create is for our Artists. It will have a unique ID for the artist.

This database will simply have an ArtistID (an integer variable) and an Artist Name (a number/name variable). Type in ArtistID for the first Column Name with data type 'int' and clear the 'allow Nulls' checkbox. This will be our primary key for this table (the items will be unique). To set this right-click the 'ArtistID' cell and choose 'Set Prmary Key' or click the Primary key icon, the one that looks like a key.

We would also like to automatically generate and increment the ArtistID number as the user adds an artist so in Column Properties, set Identity Specification (Is Identity) to Yes. The auto-increment value and starting value (seed) can be changed if necessary.

Add 'Name' for the next Column item and select nvarchar(50) (Variable-length Unicode character data) for the data type and again don't allow nulls.

Your design should be similar to figure 14.9. Save the table (File > Save Table) with a suitable name 'Artist'.

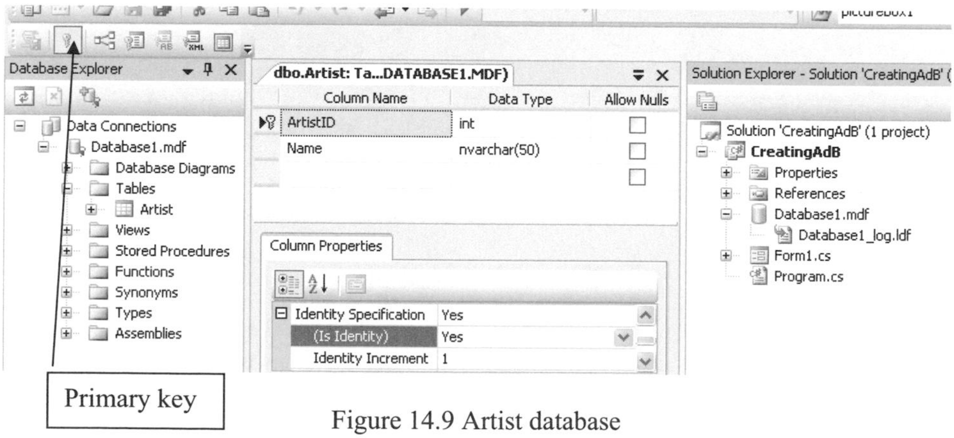

Figure 14.9 Artist database

174

The table is added to the database. If you get a timeout error, right-click tables in the Explorer and choose 'refresh'. You can now see the table in the Database/Server Explorer.

Add a second table (in Explorer, click Tables > Add New Table). Add the following column names and data types:

> ID, int, no nulls. Add the primary key and identity as before
> Title, nvarchar(100) – change the length in the properties, no nulls
> PlayingTime, datetime, allow nulls, and
> Date, datetime, allow nulls.

We also need to provide a column to link the recording to its artist. This is given the same name as the Artist primary ID.

Add a final column to the Recordings table, with name: ArtistID, data type int and don't allow nulls. The data type must match the Primary Key column we are going to link to i.e. the ArtistID in the Artist table. Your table should be similar to figure 14.10.

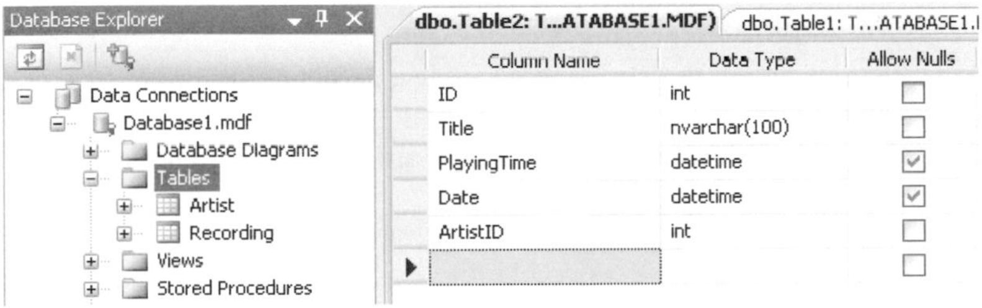

Figure 14.10 Recording table

Save the table and call it 'Recording'. We now have two tables defined: 'Artist' and 'Recording'.

14.5   Adding relationships – Database diagrams

We have created two separate tables. We now need add a relationship from the recordings to their artist. To do this we provide a link from the Recording table to the Artist table. This link is known as a foreign key and is a link from the ArtistID field in the Recording table that matches the primary key ArtistID in the Artist table. When a new recording is added to the database, the user will be forced to select an artist for the recording from the Artist table.

We can add a relationship visually using the 'Database Diagrams' in the Database/Server explorer, this is shown on the third line of the Explorer in figure 14.10.

Right click Database Diagram and select 'Add a new diagram', click 'yes' to allow the objects to be created and then select and add both the Artist and Recording tables.

The two tables are shown with their fields. To make the link, select the primary key you want to link and drag and drop it to the field in the second table. In this case we want to make a link from the Artists table primary key to the Recording Table so that when we add a recording we are forced to choose an ArtistID.

Click the ArtistID and drag this to the ArtistID in the Recording table. Note that it makes a relationship name called FK_Recording _Artist, the FK meaning 'foreign key', see figure 14.11.

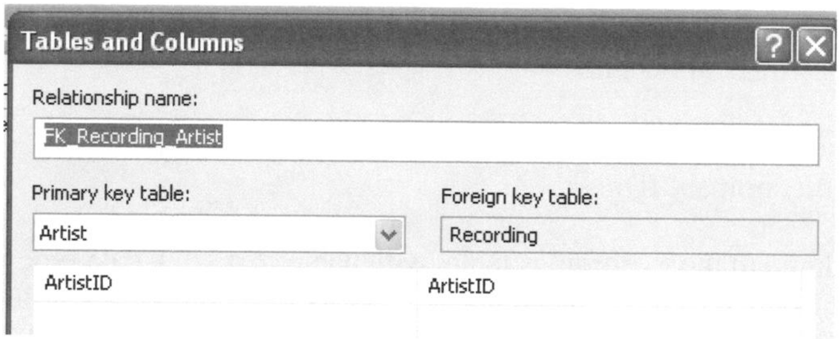

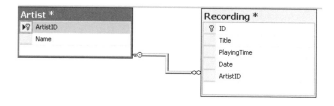

Figure 14.11 Linking tables

The database diagram shows the connection between the tables, see figure 14.12. Note the 'one to many' connection. The Artist table has the primary key, and the Recording table the 'infinity' sign, indicating that one unique artist can have unlimited recordings.

Figure 14.12 One to Many database diagram connection

Now let's add some data to our tables. We will add our artists first and then we will be forced to select one when we add our recordings.

Expand the Database/Server explorer tables to show the Artist and Recording tables. Right-click the Artist table and select 'Show Table Data', see figure 14.13. We can now add our Artists.

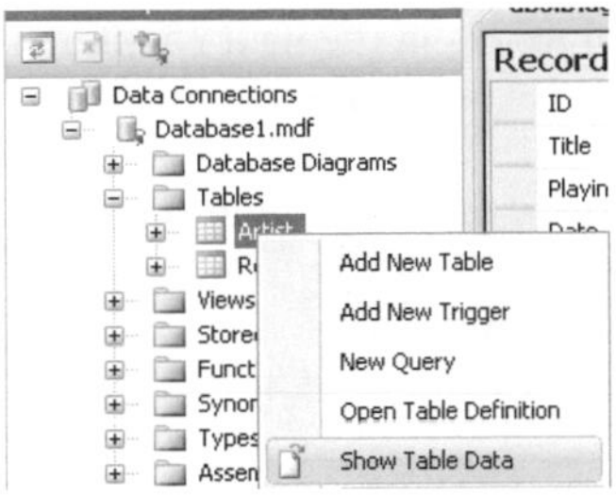

Figure 14.13 Show Table Data

Click the Name field and add some artists, e.g: Van Morrison, Rolling Stones, Bob Dylan, The Who etc, see figure 14.14. Remember the ArtistID number will be generated for you. This will be used when we link from the recording table.

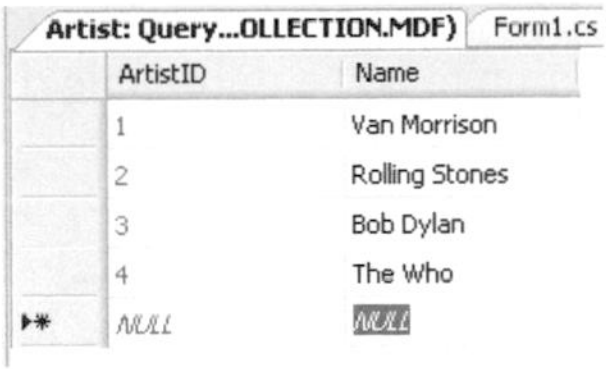

ArtistID	Name
1	Van Morrison
2	Rolling Stones
3	Bob Dylan
4	The Who
NULL	NULL

Figure 14.14 Adding Artists to Tables

Now we can add some recordings. Choose 'Show Table Data' for the Recording table and add some titles and artists. You have to use the number you want for the required artist in the ArtistID column, not the artist's name. You will get an error if you try typing in a non-existing number for ArtistID. You will also have to add a complete DateTime data type (8/7/2008 12:59:59, or 1:23:45).

Add the data as shown in figure 14.15, or make up your own titles

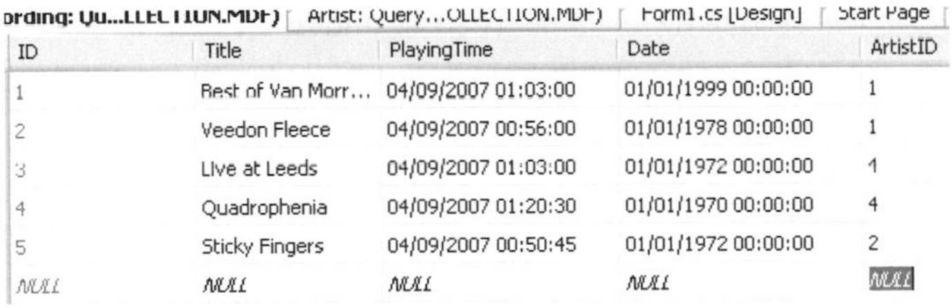

ID	Title	PlayingTime	Date	ArtistID
1	Best of Van Morr...	04/09/2007 01:03:00	01/01/1999 00:00:00	1
2	Veedon Fleece	04/09/2007 00:56:00	01/01/1978 00:00:00	1
3	Live at Leeds	04/09/2007 01:03:00	01/01/1972 00:00:00	4
4	Quadrophenia	04/09/2007 01:20:30	01/01/1970 00:00:00	4
5	Sticky Fingers	04/09/2007 00:50:45	01/01/1972 00:00:00	2
NULL	NULL	NULL	NULL	NULL

Figure 14.15 Adding recordings

If you now try to delete 'The Who' from the Artist table you will get an error message, because you have links to it from the Recording table. Visual Studio ensures data integrity.

Save the project, we will return to this in the next chapter. The Recordings database is an MDF file (recordings.mdf) and has been saved in the CreatingADb folder.

What we now need to do is display our data in our projects. We'll do that in the next chapter.

Self Assessment Exercises

1. Watch video lesson 8 'Obtaining Data from a SQL Server' pointed to by Elektor's web site.

2. Open up your Recording database in a new project. Remember it's a Microsoft SQL Server Database (MDF) file (called recordings.mdf) and has been saved in the CreatingADb folder.

3. Create another database this time with three dependent variables. You could extend your record collection to add a third table that holds a library shelf where it is stored.

4. Create a database using names as the primary key. You will of course not need a unique number as an ID, so experiment with the Identity Specification

Summary

We have discussed databases and looked at a detailed database, Microsoft's Northwind. We have seen how we can include this database in our Visual Studio projects. We have created our own database with two tables (Artist and Recording) from within Visual Studio. Each of these tables has had a primary key and a relationship was established so that when data is added, the user is forced to select an artist for each recording.

We now want our programs to display the data in the database and also write code to access the database to read, write and update the database. In the first case we want a GUI so that a user can see the items in the database and in the second case, code to access the database and add delete or search the database. We'll do that in the next chapters.

15 Displaying databases

15.1 Introduction

So far we have looked at an existing database (Northwind) and also created our own database with linked tables from within Visual Studio. Now we want to design a GUI and write a program to display the database information. We will introduce the GUI database controls, but before we do that, we'll cover some terminology

15.2 The dataset, data binding and ActiveX Data Objects (ADO.NET)

ADO.NET objects create the connection to the database, manage the communication (the requests etc.) between your application and the database and manage the data that is retrieved as a result of a database query.

The dataset. Database programs do not deal directly with the database when they run; they use a copy known as a dataset and update the database only when required. The dataset can be the whole database or a subset, and holds a collection of data tables related to each other. The DataSet is a class within ADO.NET and we will create a dataset for our program.

Data binding allows data to be retrieved and displayed automatically using the database controls. These controls know how to automatically display and update the various types of data, relieving the programmer of the task.

The binding source is responsible for displaying the current row of data on the form and making sure all the items have the correct and matching data.

We will use a wizard to add all these controls for us. They will appear in the designer tray.

To recap, the DataSet gets populated from the database. This is controlled by the TableAdapter Manager which provides the connection and knows how to update the data. The BindingSource is responsible for displaying the current row of data on the form and making sure all the items have the correct and matching data. This is summarised in figure 15.1.

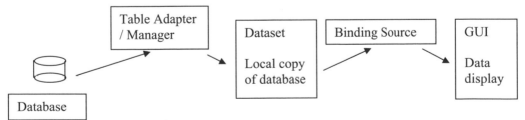

Figure 15.1 Database data transfer

We can choose to display a media-like navigator which enables us to scroll through and update the database data. You can find all these items in the ToolBox and add them yourselves, but there is a wizard that does it all that for you.

15.3   Displaying database information.

Let's return to the Northwind database and display its information in a C# project.

Start a new project and call it DisplayNorthWind.
Add a new data source (Data > Add New DataSource), select Database > New Connection, and browse for the Northwind database. Remember, Access database files have an MDB file extension, SQL Server compact 3.5 database files have an SDF extension and SQL Server database files have a MDF file extension. In this example the Access MDB database has been used.

Click 'Yes' to copy the file into your folder, select Tables and finish. See figure 15.2.

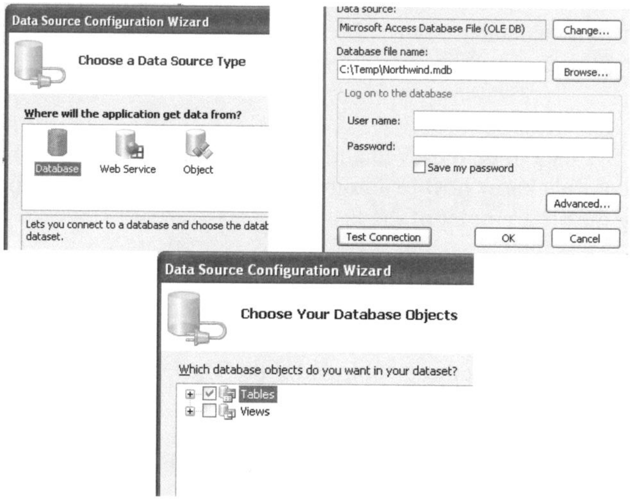

Figure 15.2. Adding a data source

Select Data > Show Data Sources from the main menu to display the data set, see figure 15.3. If the database isn't displayed, check you have completed the Data Source configuration wizard as above.

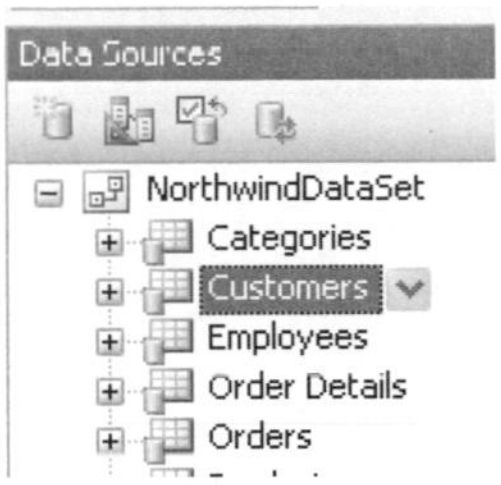

Figure 15.3 Customer Data Source

15.3.1 DataGridView

This time, we'll look at the Customers table instead of the Employees table. Click the Customers table (see figure 15.3) and from the drop down box select DataGridView, see figure 15.14.

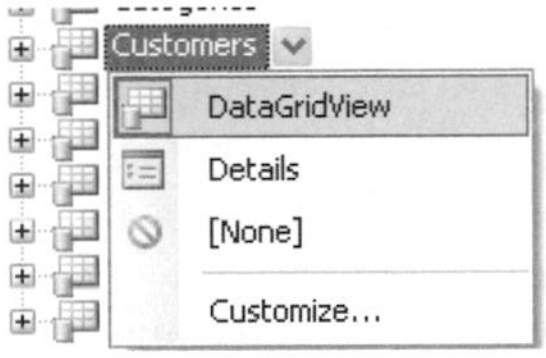

Figure 15.4 DataGrid view

The DataGridView will display all the data in a grid form. Alternatively, the Details view displays the individual data rows one at a time; we'll see that later.

Drag the Customers' table icon    onto the form. This will add a DataGridView and Navigator to the form. It will also add the DataSet, BindingSource and TableAdaptor, see figure 15.5.

Figure 15.5 Database controls

You can now run the program and see the customer database in a grid format, see figure 15.6.

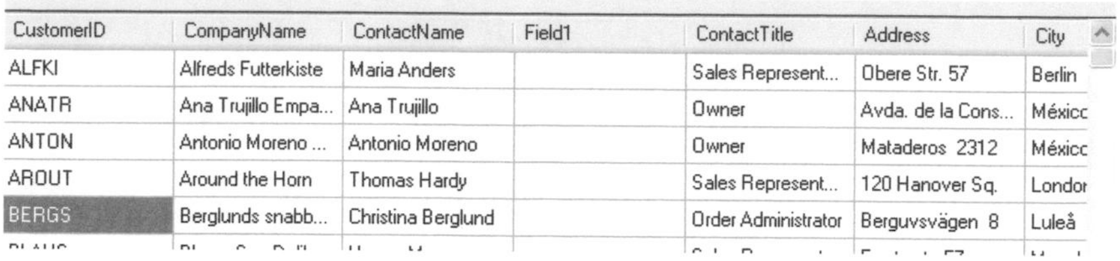

CustomerID	CompanyName	ContactName	Field1	ContactTitle	Address	City
ALFKI	Alfreds Futterkiste	Maria Anders		Sales Represent...	Obere Str. 57	Berlin
ANATR	Ana Trujillo Empa...	Ana Trujillo		Owner	Avda. de la Cons...	Méxicc
ANTON	Antonio Moreno ...	Antonio Moreno		Owner	Mataderos 2312	Méxicc
AROUT	Around the Horn	Thomas Hardy		Sales Represent...	120 Hanover Sq.	Londor
BERGS	Berglunds snabb...	Christina Berglund		Order Administrator	Berguvsvägen 8	Luleå
PLAUC						

Figure 15.6 Customer DataGrid display

It's as easy as that! You can now use the Navigator to step through the database and also add new customers and deleted them, see figure 15.7.

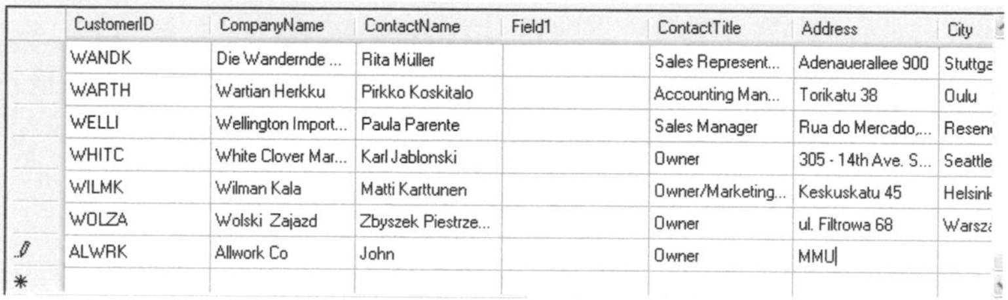

	CustomerID	CompanyName	ContactName	Field1	ContactTitle	Address	City
	WANDK	Die Wandernde ...	Rita Müller		Sales Represent...	Adenauerallee 900	Stuttgz
	WARTH	Wartian Herkku	Pirkko Koskitalo		Accounting Man...	Torikatu 38	Oulu
	WELLI	Wellington Import...	Paula Parente		Sales Manager	Rua do Mercado,...	Resene
	WHITC	White Clover Mar...	Karl Jablonski		Owner	305 - 14th Ave. S...	Seattle
	WILMK	Wilman Kala	Matti Karttunen		Owner/Marketing...	Keskuskatu 45	Helsink
	WOLZA	Wolski Zajazd	Zbyszek Piestrze...		Owner	ul. Filtrowa 68	Warsza
	ALWRK	Allwork Co	John		Owner	MMU	

Figure 15.7 Adding Data

The individual fields are checked for the correct data type when you add a new customer.

You can also save the data, but be careful. Depending on your set up, the application may get the original database the next time you run it, and so the data you saved isn't there.

Stop the program and click the tiny box with the right arrow in the top right hand corner of the DataGridView control to display the DataGridView tasks, see figure 15.8. It is here that the data source and editing options can be chosen.

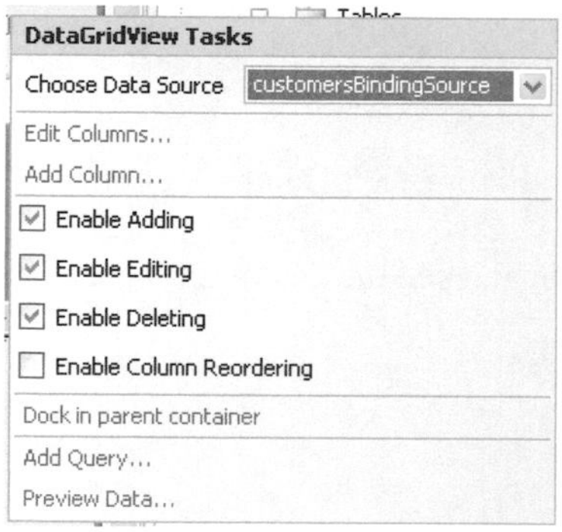

Figure 15.8 DataGridView tasks

You can edit and add columns, and enable editing, deleting and adding of new database entries by your user.

15.3.2 Details view

If you want to see how the Details view works and displays the items, repeat the above exercise in a new project and select Details instead of the DataGridView, from the drop-down box. Figure 15.9 shows the Employees Details selected, note the icon is different from the DataGridView.

Figure 15.9 Details view and icon.

Drag this to the form to show the details view on the form, see figure 15.10.

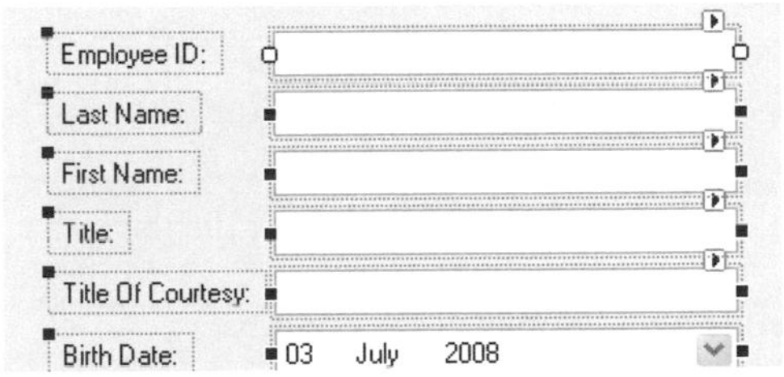

Figure 15.10 Details display

Again a navigator has been added and each of the controls has its own task that can be selected by clicking the right arrow.

Run the program and note that the employees are now displayed one at a time. The correct option appears if you want to alter or add data, for instance, the birth date appears as a DateTimePicker control, see figure 15.11.

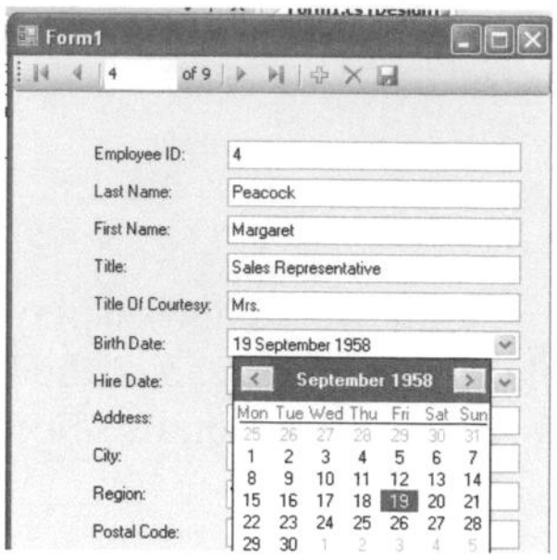

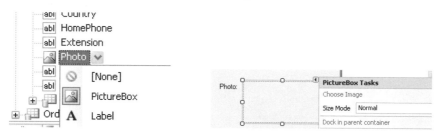

Figure 15.11 DateTimePicker

You can also display individual items from the table on the form. Expand the Employee table and select PictureBox from the available items. Place a photo on the form and click the right-arrow to see the PictureBox tasks, see figure 15.12.

Figure 15.12 PictureBox display

Run the program to see the photographs of the employees.

15.4   Viewing the data set

The dataset is the memory resident copy of the database. The individual tables of the database and how they are linked can be viewed by clicking the XSD (XML Schema Definition) file displayed in the Solution Explorer, see figure 15.13.

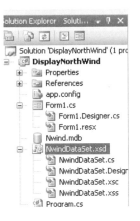

Figure 15.13 Dataset XSD file

The database tables and the links between the tables are displayed, see figure 15.14.

Figure 15.14 The DataSet

You can see the primary fields and the relationships.

15.5   Structured Query Language (SQL)

Finally we will take a look at how we might extract information using Structured Query Language,or SQL commands. If you looked at the SELECT command you would have seen how it defines the fields to extract from the database. It's something like:

SELECT CustomerID, CompanyName, ContactName, Phone FROM Customers

The SELECT command can be qualified in many ways and the basic SQL commands are shown in Table 15.1. We won't need to use any of these commands, letting the wizard generate them instead, but you might find it useful to know some of the commands to see how the data is extracted from the database.

SQL keyword	Description
SELECT	Selects fields from one or more tables
FROM	Specifies the table(s) from which to retrieve the data. - Required for SELECT and DELETE commands
WHERE	Specifies criteria that determines the rows to be retrieved
GROUP BY	Specifies criteria for grouping records
ORDER BY	Specifies criteria for ordering records
INSERT	Inserts data into a table
UPDATE	Updates data in a table
DELETE	Deletes data from a table

Table 15.1 SQL commands

We shall briefly discuss these commands.

The SELECT command.

The SELECT query is used to select or get information from a table. The basic form is:

SELECT fields FROM tableName

All the fields from the Northwind employee's table were selected using:

SELECT * FROM employees

We can select specific fields by replacing the asterisk with the field name. For example:

SELECT firstName, lastName FROM employees

The WHERE command.

In most cases users want to look for specific data with the fields. The WHERE command is used to specify the selection. The simplest format of the WHERE command is:

SELECT field FROM tableName WHERE criteria

For example to select all the users called John from the database you might use:

SELECT firstName, lastName FROM employees WHERE firstName = John

The WHERE condition can contain the usual operators ($<, >, <=, >=, ==, <>$) as well as LIKE. LIKE can be used with a wildcard. For example, to get first names beginning with J, as follows:

SELECT firstName, lastName FROM employee WHERE firstName LIKE 'J*'

The INSERT command

The INSERT command inserts a new record in a table. The simplest form for this is:

INSERT INTO tableName (fieldname(s)) VALUES (value(s))

For example:

INSERT INTO employees(firstName, lastName) VALUES ('Joe', 'ALLWORK')

The UPDATE command

Changes are made only to a local copy of the database. The UPDATE command is used to save these changes. The simplest form is:

UPDATE tableName SET fieldname = value WHERE criteria

For example:

UPDATE employees SET lastName = 'ALLWORK'
WHERE lastName = DOE and firstName = 'Jane'

This will change the last name of the record for Jane DOE to ALLWORK.

The DELETE command

The DELETE command will delete data from a table. The simplest form is:

DELETE FROM tableName WHERE criteria

For example we could delete the record for Jane ALLWORK using the command:

DELETE FROM employees WHERE firstName = 'Jane' AND lastName = 'ALLWORK'

Self Assessment Exercises

1. Watch video lesson 9 'Databinding Data to User Interface Controls' pointed to by Elektor's web site.

2. Create your own database from within Visual Studio.

3. Display the Artist and Recording tables from last chapter's database using both DataGridView and Details views.

4. Add a selection of individual items for the same table item to the form, for example for the recording date, display a DateTimePicker, a TextBox, a Label etc.

Remember, depending on how you coped your database, you may only be able to keep your saved data if your run the .EXE file, not if you re-compile from within Visual Studio.

Summary

In this chapter we have seen how data is extracted from the database with a table adaptor, creating a local memory resident copy of the database (the dataset), the items of which are displayed using controls which are binding sources, i.e. 'bound' to the data, and change automatically as the user interacts with them.

We have used the DataGridView which displays all the table's fields in a grid form and also the Details view which displays the individual fields. We have seen the DataGrid view tasks such as adding, editing and deleting. A navigator was automatically placed on the form and as the user scrolls through the database the views automatically change; they are bound to the data.

The SQL language which is used to access the data in the database has briefly been covered. In our case the wizard created the SQL statement we needed.

In the next chapter we will see how to extract the data from the database and deal with this in our code, for example to save data collected from a database.

16 Accessing a database with code

16.1 Introduction.

We have seen how to display the contents of a database, create our own database and display the data in a GUI using DataGrid and Details views. We will now see how to access the data in a database from code and either extract or add data to the database.

There is a single database walkthrough which uses Northwind on the Microsoft website at:
http://msdn.microsoft.com/en-us/library/0f92s97z.aspx.

We shall create our own general data logger database and write code to read that.

16.2 Creating the database

We will create a simple single table database and write code to navigate and update the database. We will add our own navigation buttons rather than use the Navigator tool or grid view tasks, so that you understand the process in adding, deleting and updating a database.

You can either create the database in Access and then add it to your project, or create it from within Visual Studio as we did in chapter 14. Follow either 16.2.1 'Creating the database in Access' or 16.2.2 'Creating a database from within Visual Studio' to create the data logger database. If you are unsure about any of the steps, refer back to chapter 14.

16.2.1 Creating the database in Access

Create a new database in Access (File> New > Blank database) and call it Logger. Create in design view and add columns with field name and type the following; see figure 16.1.

- ID (type: number – change to Integer). Set required to Yes, and right-click to make it a primary key;
- Setpoint: number – change to Integer;
- Temperature: number – change to single;
- Time: Date/Time – change to short Time.

Save it as LoggerTable (so the database is called Logger, and it contains one table called LoggerTable)

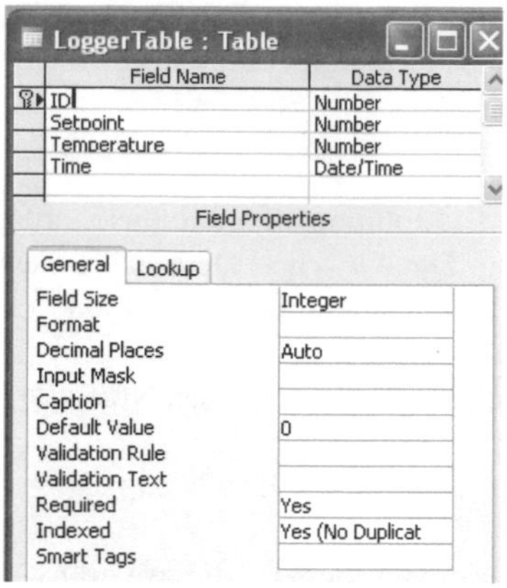

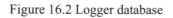

Figure 16.1 Access logger database.

Add some data to the database and save it, see figure 16.2

LoggerTable : Table

ID	Setpoint	Temperature	Time
0	10	23.5	11:15
1	11	12.5	11:16
0	0	0	

Figure 16.2 Logger database

Now continue at section 16.3, 'Displaying the Database'.

16.2.2 Creating a database from within Visual Studio

You can create a local database or Server-based database, we will create the latter, choose Project > Add New Item > Service-based Database and call it Logger, see figure 16.3.

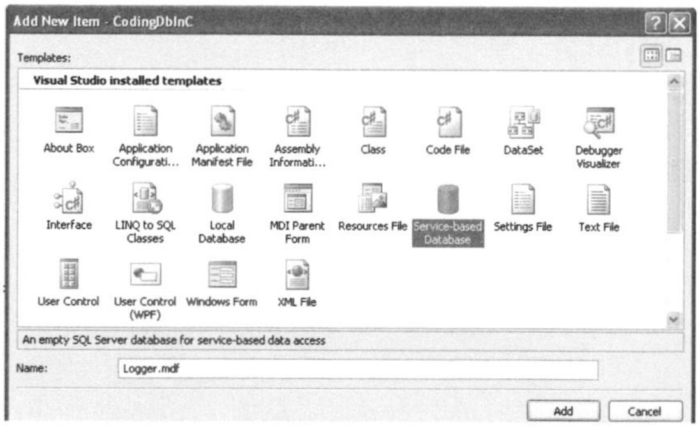

Figure 16.3 Adding a database

Note that it has an MDF extension compared with the MDB extension of an Access database. Click Finish to add data to the database later.

Display the Server/Database explorer, and right-click Tables to add a new table, see figure 16.4.

Figure 16.4 Adding a New Table

Add the data types as shown in figure 16.5. Don't allow any nulls

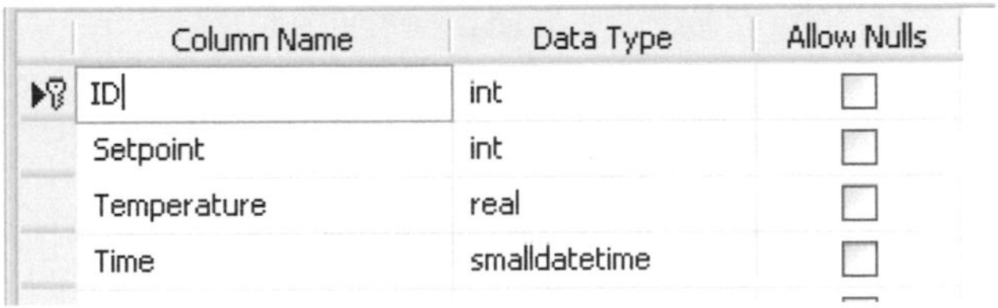

Column Name	Data Type	Allow Nulls
ID	int	☐
Setpoint	int	☐
Temperature	real	☐
Time	smalldatetime	☐

Figure 16.5 Table data types

Set the ID field's Identity Specification to 'Yes' and Is Identity to 'Yes'. Make it a primary key.

Save the table and call it LoggerTable. It will be added it to the Tables in the Logger database. Expand the tables, right-click LoggerTable and select Show Table Data. This will enable you to add data, see figure 16.6

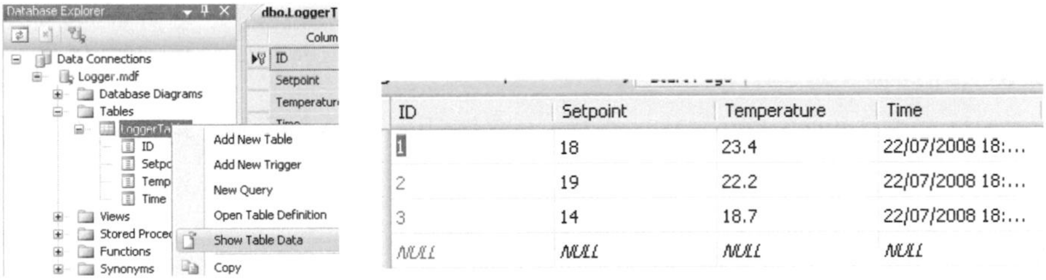

ID	Setpoint	Temperature	Time
1	18	23.4	22/07/2008 18:...
2	19	22.2	22/07/2008 18:...
3	14	18.7	22/07/2008 18:...
NULL	NULL	NULL	NULL

Figure 16.6 Adding table data

Add some data. Remember you don't have to enter data into the ID field. Save the project and close it.

16.3   Displaying the database

Now that we have a database, let's display the items before moving on to change the database. This is covered in the previous chapter, but we shall repeat it briefly here.

Start a new project. Add the Data Source connection. In Server/Database explorer, right-click DataConnections and choose Add connection. Select either the Access Database File (MDB file) or SQL Server Database (MDF file) depending on how you created your database file and browse for it. Clear the User name box, test the connection and click OK, see figure 16.7.

Figure 16.7 Adding the data source connection

16.3.1 Add the Data Source

To add the data source to the project, choose Data > Add new data source > Database. The data connection that has just been created should be selected but if not, select New Connection and follow the above process.

You may get a message asking if you would like to copy the database to your folders. If you say yes to this, a copy of the database will be made each time the program runs which means that any changes you make will be overwritten the next time you run the program.

16.3.2 Select Database Objects

The wizard now requests your database objects, see figure 16.8. Select Tables and click Finish.

Figure 16.8 Adding Database objects.

192

We now have a database called Logger with a table called LoggerTable, a connection called loggerConnectionString, a table adaptor called LoggerTableTableAdapter and a dataset (memory resident version of the database) called loggerDataSet. To refresh your memory on how these all link together, see figure 15.1. To see the individual database fields, expand the database in database explorer, see figure 16.9. To see the fields we can add to the form, expand the database in the data sources window, see figure 16.10.

Figure 16.9 Database fields

Figure 16.10 Data Sources Window

Before we add individual Details view controls, check your database access works by displaying the items in a DataGridView as we did before. Display the DataSources (Data > Show Data Sources), select the Logger table and ensure DataGridView is selected. Click and drag the Logger table to the form, see figure 16.10.

Check the DataGridView tasks (click arrow in top right-hand corner) and check the editing options as shown in figure 16.11.

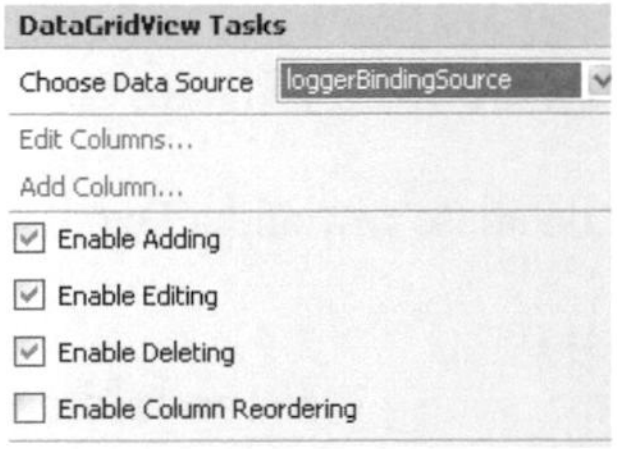

Figure 16.11 DataGridView tasks

Run the program. Because we allowed editing, you can now add data to your database by typing in the fields, see figure 16.12.

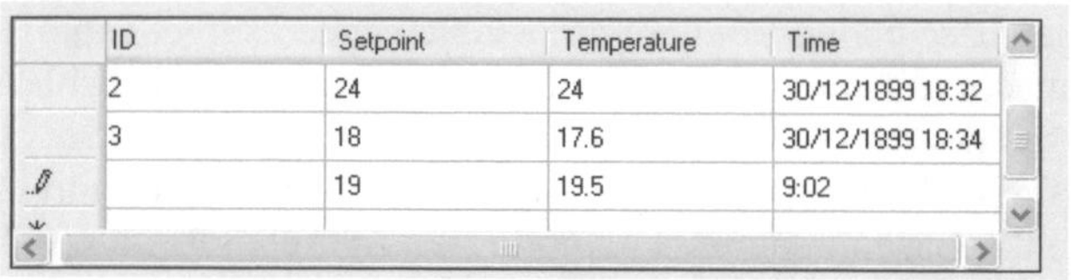

ID	Setpoint	Temperature	Time	
2	24	24	30/12/1899 18:32	
3	18	17.6	30/12/1899 18:34	
	19	19.5	9:02	

Figure 16.12 Database display

Remember that, depending on your setting, on restarting the program the original database may be obtained not the updated one.

16.3.3 Accessing the database from code

To see how we can display the database items from our code we'll add our own navigation controls, even though a navigator toolbar is available. We shall read the database values and display them using a MessageBox and add new values to the database from textboxes.

Start by adding controls so we can add data to the database. Add two labels and two textboxes to allow the user to add a new set point and temperature (call them txtSP and txtTemp).

Add buttons First, Next and Add (btnFirst, btnNext and btnAdd) so that your design is similar to figure 16.13.

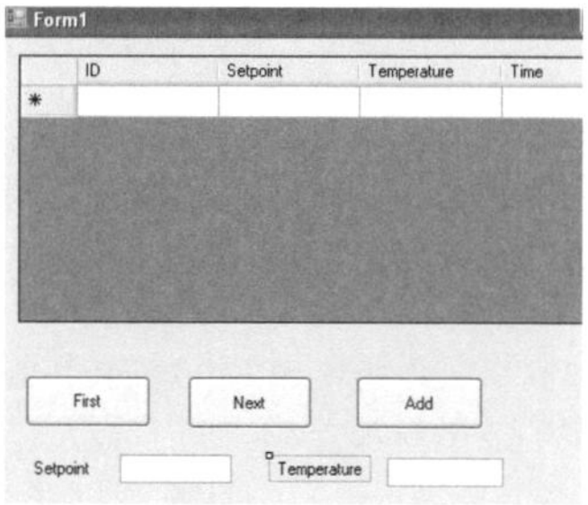

Figure 16.13 Program GUI

Declare a pointer to the current database row and a DataRow type:

```
public int rowPosition = 0;
public DataRow drAdd ;            // see later
```

The cells in the database are accessed by the row position and the column name or index, like a two dimensional array. So, if rowPosition is 0, the ID of the first row is accessed using:

```
loggerTable.Rows[rowPosition]["ID"]
```

Add the following method to display the rows. We shall call this from the First and Next button clicks.

```
private void ShowCurrentRecord()
{
  if (this.loggerDataSet.loggerTable.Rows.Count != 0)
  {
    MessageBox.Show("ID="+
this.loggerDataSet.loggerTable.Rows[rowPosition]["ID"].ToString()+
    ", Setpoint=" +
this.loggerDataSet.loggerTable.Rows[rowPosition]["Setpoint"].ToString() +
    ", Temperature=" +
this.loggerDataSet.loggerTable.Rows[rowPosition]["Temperature"].ToString() +
    ", Time=" +
this.loggerDataSet.loggerTable.Rows[rowPosition]["Time"].ToString());
  }
}
```

If you get errors when you enter this code, check the names and the case of identifiers. Let the IntelliSense prompt you.

Add the following code for the First, Next and Add buttons:

```
private void btnFirst_Click(object sender, EventArgs e)
{
    rowPosition = 0;
    ShowCurrentRecord();
}

private void btnNext_Click(object sender, EventArgs e)
{
    if (rowPosition<this.loggerDataSet.loggerTable.Rows.Count-1)
    {
        rowPosition++;
    }
    ShowCurrentRecord();
}
```

I'll let you work out how you might add 'Previous' and 'Last' buttons.

Now let's add code to add data. We use the DataRow we declared at the top and add the contents for each field. I have also added the current time.

```
private void btnAdd_Click(object sender, EventArgs e)
```

```
        {
            // check we have something to add
        if ((txtSP.Text != String.Empty) || (txtTemp.Text != String.Empty))
            {
                drAdd = this.loggerDataSet.loggerTable.NewRow();
                drAdd["ID"] = this.loggerDataSet.loggerTable.Rows.Count+1;
                drAdd["Setpoint"] = int.Parse(txtSP.Text);
                drAdd["Temperature"] = float.Parse(txtTemp.Text);
                DateTime theTime = new DateTime();
                theTime = DateTime.Now;
                drAdd["Time"] = theTime.ToShortTimeString();
                this.loggerDataSet.loggerTable.Rows.Add(drAdd);
            }
        }
```

The program should now run and you can add data to the database from your code.

16.3.4 Update the Database

At the moment only the memory resident dataset is updated. To update the database on the disk, add an Update button and the following code:

```
        private void btnUpdate_Click(object sender, EventArgs e)
        {
            try
            {
              // validate control
              this.Validate();
              // end the editing to allow update
              this.loggerTableBindingSource.EndEdit();
              // Update all the changes in the dataset
              this.tableAdapterManager.UpdateAll(this.loggerDataSet);
            }
            catch (SystemException ex)
            {
                MessageBox.Show("Update failed" + ex.ToString());
            }
        }
```

The TableAdapterManager is a new component in VS2008 that builds on the TableAdapter that was used in VS2005. If you really need to know more, search for it in Visual Studio help.

Remember that depending on how you created or copied the database, the original may not be updated. On re-running the application the original database may be retrieved. You can see this if you search for your database. You will see the original database and the copy (which is the one your program updates). For more information on this, refer to the Microsoft web site at: http://msdn.microsoft.com/en-us/library/ms233817.aspx

16.4 Reading and writing nulls in database

You may need to read or write a null in a database, rather than using a default value.

The item to check for is DBNull.Value

16.4.1 Reading Null values from a database

Null values read from a database can be converted to a string without a problem, e.g.:

```
txtTemp.Text = this.DataSet.Table.Rows[rowPosition]["temp"].ToString();
```

However, if you want to use a value such as an integer, you have to check that it's not a null entry on the database before using it. For example the following code will check for a null in the database and use the (integer) value if not:

```
if (this.DataSet.Table.Rows[rowPosition]["sp"] != DBNull.Value)
{
  int tempSP = (int)this.DataSet1.Table.Rows[rowPosition]["sp"];
}
```

Of course, if you want to use a default value instead of a null you can do so, just add an else clause. (else tempSP = -1;)

16.4.2 Writing Null values to a database

In this example a floating point value is read from a textbox. If the textbox is empty, dbNull.Value is saved in the database, otherwise the textbox's value is used:

```
if (txtTemp.Text == String.Empty)
{
  drAdd["temp"] = DBNull.Value;
}
  else
{
  drAdd["temp"] = float.Parse(txtTemp.Text);
}
```

Self Assessment Exercises

1. Take another look at video lesson 9 'Databinding Data to User Interface Controls' pointed to by Elektor's web site.

2. Add buttons in the program for Last and Previous commands.

3. Write a program that automatically generates a set point, a temperature and a time, say on a Timer event, and adds these values to the database.

4. Create your own database and add values to it.

Summary

In this chapter we have seen how to create a database from within Visual Studio and to add this data source to a program. Initially the data was displayed using a DataGridView and navigator controls as we did in the last chapter, but this time we have added our own navigation controls and read the database using the database table property with row and column, and written to the database using DataRow data type.

Now we know how to access data in a database, we will now see how to plot the data, or in fact plot any data points.

17 Plotting and Charts

17.1 Introduction

As we have seen, .NET does not have any plotting controls or classes. In this chapter we will see how to use a third party add-on called NPlot. This is available from the NPlot Wiki site: www.netcontrols.org. Documentation is available at: netcontrols.org/nplot/downloads/nplot_introduction.pdf.

17.2 Plotting with Nplot

Nplot provides a selection of charts, including line plot, point plot, step plot, candle plot, bar plot and image plot. They are shown in figure 17.1

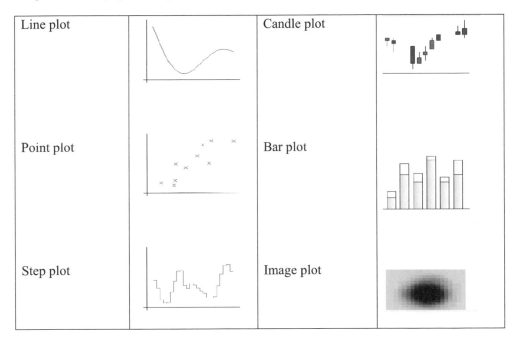

Line plot		Candle plot	
Point plot		Bar plot	
Step plot		Image plot	

Figure 17.1 Types of plot

We shall see how to define the type of plot, data, axes, scales etc. in this chapter.

17.3 Obtaining the software

To obtain the software, download and extract the zipped file from the web site at:

http://netcontrols.org/nplot/wiki/index.php?n=Main.DownloadArea

Although the readme file says to download MSBee, this is not really necessary.

17.4 Adding NPlot to your project

Having downloaded and extracted the file, you need to add the Nplot classes to your project. The process is summarised here, but you can also follow the Windows Forms Tutorial (C#) on the NPlot wiki web site, see figure 17.2.

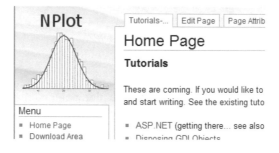

Figure 17.2 Nplot Wiki web site

1. Open Visual Studio and create or open your project.

2. Open the toolbox and right click on any item. Select Choose Items ...

3. Select the .Net Framework Components tab, click Browse.

4. Find the extracted NPlot folder and open the bin > net > 2.0 > release folder and select NPlot.dll. Click open.

5. Make sure the PlotSurface2D control is checked and click OK, see figure 17.3.

6. The PlotSurface2D control appears in the toolbox, and you can now use it like any other toolbox control.

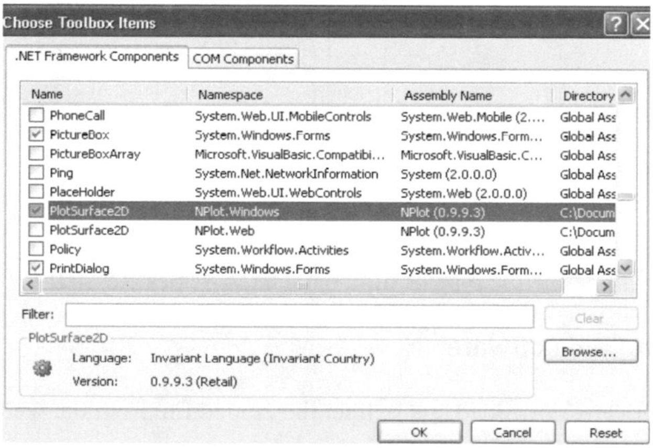

Figure 17.3 .NET components

You also need to make sure your project includes a reference to the NPlot library.

Open the solutions explorer and expand References. Make sure Nplot is referenced, see figure 17.4. If not, right click the References header and select Add Reference. Click Browse and locate the NPlot dll file (NPlot folder>bin>net>2.0>release). Click OK.

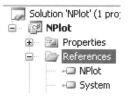

Figure 17.4 NPlot reference

17.5   NPlot Windows Form Tutorial

Having done all that, you can follow the rest of the NPlot tutorial on the NPlot wiki web site. Figure 17.5 shows the graphs generated.

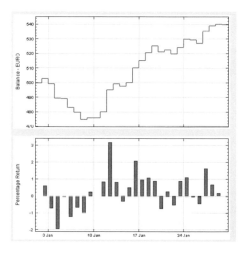

Figure 17.5 NPlot Windows Tutorial display.

For a more dynamic display, set the DateTimeToolTip property for each control to true. The DateTimeToolTip changes the date display as the cursor is moved over the graph.

17.6   Drawing a graph

Let's find out more about the coding and how to draw a graph. If you're like me, you most probably having thought about the process of drawing a graph since you were at school. You have to work out what the range of values are for the axes, what scales you are going to use and their labels, the grid (horizontal and vertical), the size and colour of the pen and the data values themselves. All of these need to be defined in your code when drawing the graph.

The axes that are available are shown in figure 17.6:

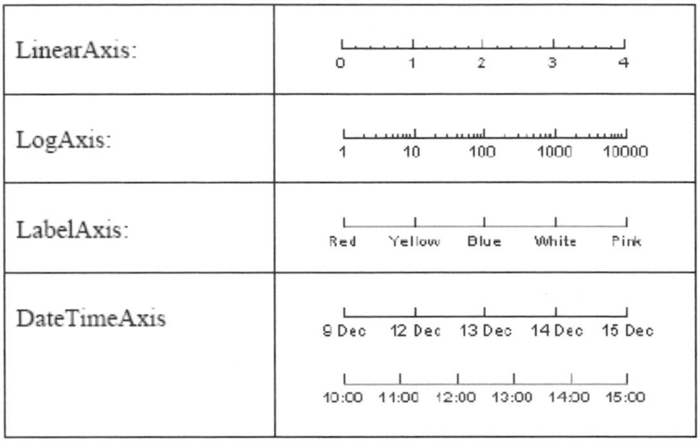

Figure 17.6 NPlot axes

The axes' scales are automatically determined, but you might want to add a label, tick text, and the angle of the text.

At this stage we should also mentioned how the data is specified. The following can be used:

1. A DataSet, DataTable or DataView. (Useful for databases)
2. A collection:
      a. Double[ ]
      b. System.Collections.ArrayList
      c. System.Collections.Generic.List<Int16>

We will use a List collection to hold our X and Y data values.

17.7 Graph exercise.

Let's try plotting the graph of sineX/X. This is quite a pretty graph. It has a maximum X value of +1. And we shall plot it over ±50 radians. We'll start with a step plot and then change it to a line plot.

Start a new project. Add **using NPlot**; at the top of the code. Check that Nplot is shown in the references.

Add a plotSurface2D control on the form. Change its name to plotSurfaceSineX.

We'll draw the grid first. Add the following code after InitializeComponent( );

```
// clear the surface
 plotSurfaceSineX.Clear();

//Add a background grid.
 Grid grid = new Grid();
 grid.VerticalGridType = Grid.GridType.Coarse;
 grid.HorizontalGridType = Grid.GridType.Coarse;
 grid.MajorGridPen = new Pen(Color.LightGray, 1.0f);

 plotSurfaceSineX.Add(grid);
```

You can of course be lead by the IntelliSense and see the other options available.

Follow the code you have typed with code for a step-plot graph – we shall see how to get a smooth curve later.

```
//Create a step plot instance for the sineX chart.
 StepPlot stepBalance = new StepPlot();
 // choose Pen colour and size
 stepBalance.Pen = new Pen(Color.Blue, 2);
```

Now add the lists to which the points will be added and from which be drawn. There are two, one for the X-axis and one for the Y-axis (SineX/X).

```
//Create the lists from which to pull data.
 List<float> XAxis = new List<float>();
 List<float> sineXoverX = new List<float>();
```

Now let's add the X values and calculate the Y:

```
//Add data to X axis lists.
 float range = 50.0F;
 float f = -range;
 while (f<=range)      // start at -50.0
 {
     XAxis.Add(f);      // add the X value
     f=f+0.5F;
     // and calculate Yvalues – check we don't divide by zero
     if (f == 0)
     {
         sineXoverX.Add(1);
     }
     else
     {
```

```
        sineXoverX.Add((float)Math.Sin(f) / f);
    }
}
```

Now we set up the data source and X axis for the plot and add to the plot. Note that this uses the step plot object, stepBalance that we declared above.

```
//Set the x-axis (abscissa) and datasource for the plot.
  stepBalance.AbscissaData = XAxis;
  stepBalance.DataSource = sineXoverX;

//Add the stepBalance to plot.
  plotSurfaceSineX.Add(stepBalance);
```

Set up the general plot settings:

```
// Plot general settings.
  plotSurfaceSineX.ShowCoordinates = true;
  plotSurfaceSineX.YAxis1.Label = "SineX over X";
  plotSurfaceSineX.YAxis1.LabelOffsetAbsolute = true;
  plotSurfaceSineX.YAxis1.LabelOffset = 40;
  plotSurfaceSineX.XAxis1.HideTickText = false; // true;
  plotSurfaceSineX.Padding = 5;
```

And finally refresh the surface to draw it;

```
//Refresh surface.
  plotSurfaceSineX.Refresh();
```

All this code has been added in the public Form1() { code. If you now run the program, you should get a plot like figure 17.7:

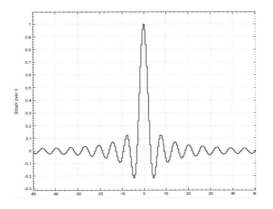

Figure 17.7 SineX/X step plot

Let's try some different plot types. Try a point plot, replace the code

```
StepPlot stepBalance = new StepPlot( );
```
with:
```
PointPlot stepBalance = new PointPlot( );
stepBalance.Pen = new Pen(Color.Black, 2);
```

This displays a point plot as shown in figure 17.8.

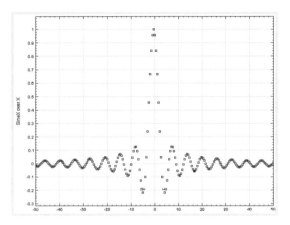

Figure 17.8 Point plot

Or for a smooth graph, see figure 17.9, replace the same lines with a Line Plot:

```
LinePlot stepBalance = new LinePlot();
stepBalance.Pen = new Pen(Color.Blue, 2);
```

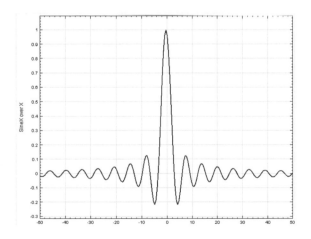

Figure 17.9 Point plot

Self Assessment Exercises

1. Now that you know the basic process for plotting a graph, try adding a legend for the X axis.

2. Draw individual graphs of:

        a) $y = \log(x)$;
        b) $y = x\text{-}5$;

3. Try to draw the graphs on the same graph and see if there is a solution to the equation:

        $x\text{-}5 = \log(x)$;

4. Try different data sources for your graph such as a double[] array, or a database dataset.

Summary

We have introduced a third party plot control from NPlot. We have seen the types of plots this can draw. We downloaded and added the control to the toolbox and followed the NPlot tutorial to seen it running. We have written our own program to plot a graph on a form.

18 Dynamic link libraries (DLL) and using Windows API

18.1 Introduction

You will soon have written some useful methods which you may want to use in other programs. Of course you could cut and paste the code into each new program, but there is a better way. By saving your code as a dynamic link library (DLL) and providing a link to it from you new program, you can just call it. The code will be loaded by the program when needed. Be careful however, if at that time it's not available you will get a run-time error so you must include it with your executable.

18.2 Writing a DLL

Let's try this with a simple example. Let's take the method we used in the chapter on Methods, which to take an integer and return its square root. The method is:

```
double SquareRoot ( int intRoot)
{
  return Math.Sqrt(intRoot);
}
```

We create our DLL by starting a new project, but this time choosing Class Library. Give it a sensible name. As you can see in figure 18.1, the name MyMathDLL is used.

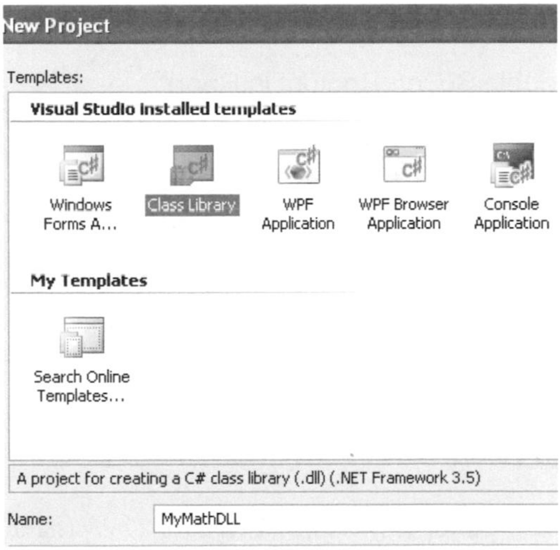

Figure18.1 Creating a DLL

The following code with Class1 is created. We will add our own class and delete Class1.

```
namespace MyMathDLL
{
    public class Class1
    {
    }
}
```

Add a new Class (Project>Add Class) and give it the name MyMathClass, see figure 18.2

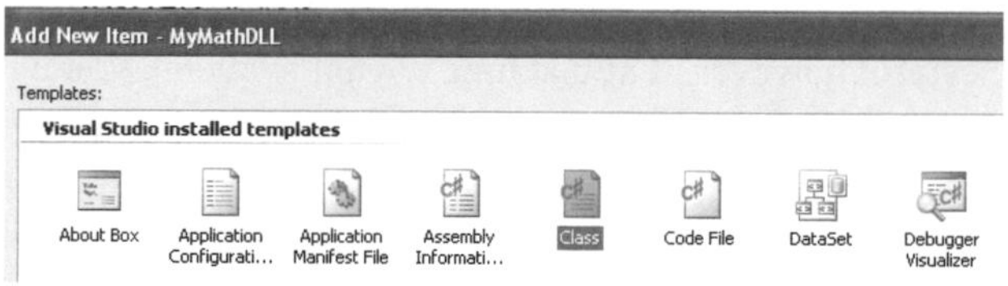

Figure 18.2 Adding a new DLL class

Remove Class1.cs by selecting it in the solution explorer and pressing the delete key.

Add the SquareRoot method to our class as shown below and save the project. The class must be declared public. We could add further mathematics classes in MyMathDLL. You might want to save all your DLLs in their own folder.

```
namespace MyMathDLL
{
    public class MyMathClass
    {
        public double SquareRoot(int intRoot)
        {
            return Math.Sqrt(intRoot);
        }
    }
}
```

Build your DLL solution (press the F6 key) and save the project. Note that if you try to run the program, you will get an error message that says the Class Library cannot be started directly.

18.3   Calling the DLL

Start a new Windows application (myMathDLLDemo). This program will call our DLL code.

We'll make it really simple and display the square root in a message box when a button is clicked.

You have to let your program know about your DLL. Add the using statement at the top of the code:

```
using MyMathDLL;
```

Add the DLL to the References. Use Project > Add reference, click the Browse tab, and browse for MyMathDLL.dll (it's in bin > release). You can now see it in References in the solution explorer, see figure 18.3

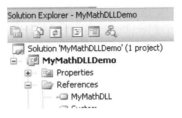

Figure 18.3 MyMathDLL reference

Add a button to a form and for the button click, change the code to the following:

```
private void button1_Click(object sender, EventArgs e)
{
  MyMathClass myMathObj = new MyMathClass();
  MessageBox.Show((myMathObj.SquareRoot(5)).ToString());
}
```

Note that the IntelliSense knows about MyMathClass and the SquareRoot method and prompts as you type, see figure 18.4. If the SquareRoot method isn't displayed, check that both the class and the method were originally declared as public.

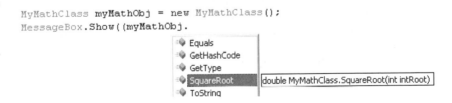

Figure 18.4 The IntelliSense display

Run the program to check it works. Your display should be similar to figure 18.5.

Figure 18.5 Program output

18.4   Static Classes

In this case we had to make an object before we could use it. We don't have to do this for the normal Math methods, so how can we do this for ours? If you remember, declaring a method as 'static' let's us do this.

Return to the MathDLL and add the Square method as follows:

```
static public double Square(double dblSquare)
{
    return dblSquare * dblSquare;
}
```

Build the project and save it.

Return to myMathDLLDemo and change the code to the following:

```
private void button1_Click(object sender, EventArgs e)
{
    // declare math object
    MyMathClass myMathObj = new MyMathClass();
    // use Square root method
    double mySqRt5 = myMathObj.SquareRoot(5);
    // square it - no need to instantiate
    double fiveSquared = MyMathDLL.MyMathClass.Square(mySqRt5);
    // and display
    MessageBox.Show(fiveSquared.ToString());
}
```

We still have to instantiate the myMathObj object from the MyMathClass, but we can now use the Square method without instantiating any objects. We have used this directly with the code:

```
MyMathDLL.MyMathClass.Square(mySqRt5);
```

Note that as you type, the IntelliSense knows about the Square method but not the SquareRoot, see figure 18.6.

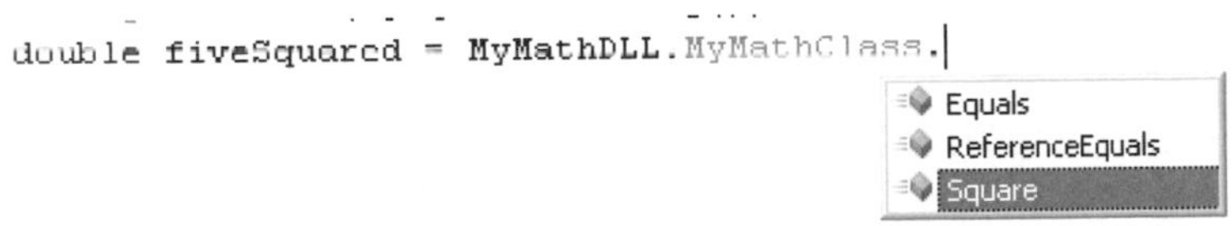

```
double fiveSquared = MyMathDLL.MyMathClass.
```

    Equals
    ReferenceEquals
    Square

Figure 18.6 Square method

18.5 Windows Application Program Interface (API)

This is a good point to introduce the Windows Application Programming Interface and the DLL calls provided that enable access to the Windows operating system and Windows services such as file handling, mouse and keyboard interfacing. Of course many of these can be made through the .NET libraries, but .NET programs run slower than truly compiled programs such as C++ and programs that use API calls run faster.

The API calls are held in three main namespaces:

- Base services – file systems, threads, error handling (kernel32.dll)
- Graphics devices interface – output to output devices and to draw windows and dialog boxes (gdi32.dll)
- User interface – manages windows and controls, mouse and keyboard inputs (user32.dll)

It is easy to use the API calls once you know what calls are available and they are described at the Platform Invoke web site at www.pinvoke.net, which also has examples.

Pinvoke.net also a Visual Studio add-in that enables programmers to access the calls directly.

18.6 Using Win API calls

The API calls are held in an external library, so add the namespace:

```
using System.Runtime.InteropServices;
```

Declare the API call. For example to add the call to make your computer beep, add the declaration:

```
[DllImport("User32.dll")]
static extern Boolean MessageBeep(UInt32 beepType);
```

(Note that's DLLImport, not DLLLmport or DIIImport)

In this case the MessageBeep is held in the User32.DLL library, it's a static member and is implemented externally (extern). In this case it is passed a UInt32 data type, and returns nothing.

211

To call the MessageBeep API, add the code (say on a button click):

```
MessageBeep(0);
```

18.7 MessageBox API example

As an example, let's call the MessageBox API. This is similar to the MessageBox.Show call we are familiar with.

Start a new project and add the following using clause at the top of the code:

```
using System.Runtime.InteropServices;
```

Before 'public Form1()', add the DLL declaration code:

```
[DllImport("User32.dll")]
public static extern int MessageBox(int h, string m, string c, int type);
```

Add a button to a form and add the following code:

```
MessageBox(0, "API Message", "API title", 0);
```

Figure 18.7 MessageBox API call

Run the program to check it works and displays the message box shown in figure 18.7.

18.8 Playing sounds

We can play wav files using the PlaySound API. Use the DLL declaration:

```
[DllImport("winmm.dll")]
public static extern long PlaySound(string lpszName, long hModule, long dwFlags);
```

To play the sound use the code:

```
PlaySound("C:\\WINDOWS\\Media\\tada.wav", 0, 1);
```

How do we find out in which DLL group our call is? If you type the call into pinvoke's search, you should find it. For instance, see figure 18.8 shows the results for the MessageBeep search, and that it's in the user32 library.

Figure 18.8 Pinvoke search result

A DLL can optionally define an entry point. We will see this in the hardware interfacing chapter where we use the input / output DLL (inpout.dll) which has two entry points: one for input and one for output.

18.9 Unsafe code

Unsafe code allows us direct access to memory and generally involves the use of pointers. You should not use unsafe code if you can help it, but sometimes it is unavoidable. For instance:

- When real time applications need to enhance performance
- For external functions and some Windows APIs
- In debugging, when we need to access memory

As an example of using unsafe code, we shall look at the GetComputerName API call. This uses a pointer to pass both a buffer and the buffer's size. To run the unsafe

As usual start a new project, add using System.Runtime.InteropServices; and add the DLL declaration, before the code public Form1( ):

```
[DllImport("Kernel32.dll")]
static extern unsafe bool GetComputerName(byte* lpBuffer, long* nSize);
```

Add a button on the form, and change its click code to:

```
private void button1_Click(object sender, EventArgs e)
{
    byte[] byteArray = new byte[512];
    long size = byteArray.Length;
    unsafe
    {
        long* pSize = &size;
        fixed (byte* pBuffor = byteArray)
        {
            GetComputerName(pBuffor, pSize);
```

213

```
        }
    }
    System.Text.Encoding textEnc =
        new System.Text.ASCIIEncoding();
    MessageBox.Show("Computer name: " +
        textEnc.GetString(byteArray));
}
```

To compile the unsafe code, open the project's Properties page. (Project > programName Properties), click the Build property page and select the 'Allow Unsafe Code' check box.

Compile and run the program – it should display your computer's name, see figure 18.9.

Figure 18.9 GetComputerName display

18.10 DLL for measuring time

There are two ways we know of measuring time: the timer component and the Ticks property of the DateTime structure. The resolution of these is stated as 1 ms and 100ns respectively. But, due to overheads you never get this resolution, it's more like 16ms.

If your system supports a high-resolution counter, it is possible to get a better resolution using the QueryPerformanceCounter and QueryPerformanceFrequency DLLs. These provide a much more accurate measurement of time. These calls are defined in the Kernel32 library. Detailed information is found at:
http://support.microsoft.com/default.aspx?scid=KB;en-us;Q172338

To use these components you need to know what clock frequency is being used to clock the counter, and then you can read the counter and hence calculate the time between counter values. The following exercise will display the clock frequency and the minimum resolution (the time taken to read the counter).

Start a new project and add using System.Runtime.InteropServices; at the top of your code. Add the following DLL declarations:

```
[DllImport("kernel32.dll")]
extern static short QueryPerformanceCounter(ref long x);

[DllImport("kernel32.dll")]
extern static short QueryPerformanceFrequency(ref long x);
```

214

The long data types are passed by ref.

For a button click event code add the following:

```
long count1 = 0, count2 = 0, freq = 0;
```

```
// if the Performance counter returns a value other than zero, there must be one
    if (QueryPerformanceCounter(ref count1) != 0)        // Begin timing.
    {
        QueryPerformanceFrequency(ref freq);             // find frequency
        QueryPerformanceCounter(ref count1);             // read counter
        QueryPerformanceCounter(ref count2);             // and read again

        MessageBox.Show("Start Value: " + count1 +
            ". End Value: " + count2 + "\r\n" +
            "Clock frequency is: " + freq + "\r\n" +
            "Resolution: 1/freq = " + (int)1000000000 / freq +
            " nanoseconds." + "\r\n" + "Time to read counter: " +
            (count2 - count1) * 1.0 / freq + " seconds.");
    }
    else
        MessageBox.Show("High-resolution counter not supported.");
```

Figure 18.10 shows the output for my PC. As you can see the clock frequency is 3.5MHz, giving a resolution of 279 nanoseconds, but actually takes 1.95 microseconds to read the performance counter, so this is the best timing I can get.

Figure 18.10 Performance frequency and counter

We will use this in more detail in the hardware chapter.

Self Assessment Exercises:

DLL
1. Add some extra Math classes. It doesn't matter if they are already defined in the Math namespace. Try adding DLLs that need to be instantiated and some that don't i.e. that are declared as static.

API

2. Look at some of the API calls at the pinvoke web site. Search for the Beep API. Note that it can be overridden to include a frequency and duration:

```
static extern bool Beep(uint dwFreq, uint dwDuration);
```

3. Write a program to play a beep of your own frequency and duration

Timing

4. Write a program to read find out the resolution of your PC using ticks and DateTime.Now. Compare this with the resolution obtained with the performance APIs

Summary

We have seen how we can create a Windows Library class and add methods, thus saving them as Dynamic Link and Locate (DLL) code. We have seen how we add the DLL reference and call the DLL code from other projects. We have also seen that by declaring a method as static, we don't have to instantiate an object to use the method.

We have covered Windows API calls and seen how they allow us direct access to the operating system, using some simple examples. We have discussed using unsafe code. Finally we have seen how we can use the Performance frequency and Performance counter to obtain better timings from our PC.

19   Hardware interfacing

19.1   Introduction

In this chapter we will look at the traditional serial and parallel ports and see how we can interface to them using the serial IO control in Visual Studio and through DLL calls. We will look at an analogue to digital hardware design that interfaces through the parallel port and design a program that turns the PC into an oscilloscope. In the next chapter we will see how we can interface to the USB port.

19.2   The Serial and Parallel ports.

The serial and parallel ports have served designers well over the life of the PC, and although are being replaced by USB are still a good way of connecting hardware to a PC.

There is plenty of information on these ports, so apart from the pin connections described later, no further detail will be provided. We will however get some idea of how to interface to these ports from our C# programs.

19.3   Visual Studio Serial Port control

Visual Studio has a control that performs serial input and output. It is the SerialPort control and found in the Components toolbox tab, see figure 19.1.

Figure 19.1 The Serial Port control

It is a non visual control. Its main properties are set to a common communications rate and are: BaudRate: 9600, DataBits: 8, Parity: None, PortName: COM1, StopBits: One.

Its main event is: DataReceived - Raised when data is received from the port

19.4   Serial Port example program

The SerialPort control can easily be demonstrated with a connector plugged into the serial port that has transmit and receive pins (2 and 3) connected together

Start a new program and call it SerialPortIO. Don't call it serialIO, as this may get confused with the namespace with that name.

This program will read data typed into a text box and send it to the serial port and display the data received by the serial port in a list box.

Place a list box, a textbox and a SerialPort control from the components toolbox on the form; use the default names.

Make sure the SerialPort's properties are set to the defaults above. You may have to change COM1: to another COM port if it's already being used.

The SerialPort class is in the System.IO.Ports namespace, so add the 'using' statement at the top of the code:

```
using System.IO.Ports;
```

Change the form load event to the following. Of course we don't have to set these properties in the code, but it's an example of how we use the Parity and StopBits enumerated data types defined in System.IO.Ports.

```
private void Form1_Load(object sender, EventArgs e)
{
    serialPort1.BaudRate = 9600;
    serialPort1.DataBits = 8;
    serialPort1.Parity = (Parity)Enum.Parse(typeof(Parity), "None");
    serialPort1.StopBits = (StopBits)Enum.Parse(typeof(StopBits), "One");
    serialPort1.Open();
}
```

We will use the serial port's WriteLine and ReadLine methods to send and read the data. Find the text box's key down event and change its code to the following:

```
private void textBox1_KeyDown(object sender, KeyEventArgs e)
{
    if (e.KeyCode == Keys.Enter)
    {
        serialPort1.WriteLine(textBox1.Text);
        listBox1.Items.Add(serialPort1.ReadLine());
        textBox1.Clear();
    }
}
```

Run the program. When the Enter key is pressed the data in the textbox is sent to the serial port using the WriteLine method. The echoed data is read by the ReadLine method and the data is displayed in the list box.

Of course, this program should really be written using threads, with one thread for the WriteLine and one for the ReadLine.

Alternatively the SerialPort's DataReceived event can be used. This runs as a thread and so to write directly to the listbox in the form load event, add the code:

218

'CheckForIllegalCrossThreadCalls = false;'

Add the following to the SerialPort's dataReceived event, and remove the
listBox.Items.Add from the keydown event.

```
private void serialPort1_DataReceived(object sender,
SerialDataReceivedEventArgs e)
{
    listBox1.Items.Add(serialPort1.ReadLine() );
}
```

The program should run and echo the data as before.

This program also works with USB to serial adaptors, but you have to change the serial
port PortName from COM1 to something like COM17.

19.5   Serial Port connections

For completeness, I have included the serial port connections. A PC may have a 25-way
or 9-way 'D' type connector. Both pin-outs are shown in Table 19.1.

Signal Name	9-way connection	25-way connection
n/c	1	1
RxD	2	3
TxD	3	2
DTR /	4	20
0V GND	5	7
DSR /	6	6
RTS /	7	4
CTS /	8	5
n/c	9	

Table 19.1 Serial port connections

Note that if you want to connect two computers together, you have to connect pin 2 on
one PC to pin 3 on the other, and vice versa. You can generally manage with using just
pins 2, 3 and a ground.

19.5   The parallel printer interface.

There have been a few designs of parallel interface during the life of the PC and so it is
difficult to know which your user may have. The original was controlled by the following
registers:

Data register: Bits 0-7 data

Status Register: Bits: 0-2 not used, 3-Error, 4-Select, 5-paper out, 6-acknowledge, 7 busy.
Control Register: Bits: 0 strobe, 1-Auto-feed, 2-initialise, 3-select, 4-IRQ enable, 5-7 N/A

The LPT1 parallel port base address (data register) is at 0x378, with status and control at 0x379 and 0x37A respectively.

To send data to a printer the data is written to the data register and the strobe line is pulsed. However instead of driving a printer, the port can be used to control input and output lines. But whilst there are eight outputs only those from the status register are guaranteed inputs.

19.6 Printer port connections

The printer port connections are shown in Table 19.2

PC -25 way D socket	Signal	Direction	Centronics Printer 36 way
1	Strobe/	→	1
2	Data 0	→	2
3	Data 1	→	3
4	Data 2	→	4
5	Data 3	→	5
6	Data 4	→	6
7	Data 5	→	7
8	Data 6	→	8
9	Data 7	→	9
10	Acknowledge/	←	10
11	Busy	←	11
12	Paper out	←	12
13	Select	←	13
14	Auto Feed	→	14
15	Error/	→	15
16	Initialise/	→	16
17	Select input/	→	17
18 -25	GND		19 -36

Table 19.2 Printer port lines

19.7 Accessing the parallel port

The parallel port can be accessed using the inout32.dll which is available from Jan Axelson's Lake View Research useful web site (www.lvr.com). The DLL provides direct read and write of the I/O ports and so could be used to drive the serial port. The file is at: http://www.lvr.com/files/.

You have to put the inpout32.dll file into your debug or release folder.

Let's design a program that will light some LEDs attached to the parallel port.

19.7.1 The hardware

To display the output of the parallel port, just attach some LEDs to it. They should be connected from pins 2 to 9 to ground (pins 18 - 25). LEDs with integral resistors are now available which makes it simple. If you don't use them, you will have to include resistor of about 470Ω for each LED.

19.7.2 The software

Our design will have eight buttons, the colour of which (red or grey) will reflect the state of the LEDs attached to the parallel port.

Start a new project and place 8 buttons on the form. For each of these set the BackColor to Web > Grey. I have given each of the buttons text: bit0, bit1 etc. Bit0 is on the right, see figure 19.2.

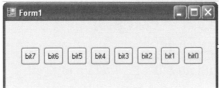

Figure 19.2 Parallel port GUI

When we click a button we will change the state of the LED and the colour of the button to match the LED.

Start a new project. Add 'using System.Runtime.InteropServices;' at the top of the code so that we can use DLLImport.

After the code: public partial class Form1 : Form {, add the following class code so that we can call the DLL:

```
public class PortIO
{
  [DllImport("inpout32.dll", EntryPoint = "Out32")]
  public static extern void Output(int adress, int value);
}
```

And if you haven't done so, place the inpout32.dll in the debug or release folder.

Declare the variables:

```
int ledState = 0;                          // record of the output state
const int BASEADDRESS = 0x378;             // Parallel port base address
```

Now add the reset code in the form load event:

```
// reset port and remember state of LEDs
ledState = 0;
PortIO.Output(BASEADDRESS, ledState);
button1.BackColor = Color.Grey;
button2.BackColor = Color.Grey;
button3.BackColor = Color.Grey;
button4.BackColor = Color.Grey;
button5.BackColor = Color.Grey;
button6.BackColor = Color.Grey;
button7.BackColor = Color.Grey;
button8.BackColor = Color.Grey;
```

and for each button click add the set/reset code:

```
//Button1 (bit 0) Button Click code
if (button1.BackColor == Color.Red)
{
    button1.BackColor = Color.Grey;
    ledState = ledState & 0xFE;    // turn bit 0 off
}
else
{
    button1.BackColor = Color.Red;
    ledState = ledState | 0x01;      // turn bit 0 on
}
PortIO.Output(BASEADDRESS, ledState);

//Button 2 (bit 1) Button Click code
if (button2.BackColor == Color.Red)
{
    button2.BackColor = Color.Grey;
    ledState = ledState & 0xFD;    // turn bit 1 off
}
else
{
    button2.BackColor = Color.Red;
    ledState = ledState | 0x02;      // turn bit 1 on
}
PortIO.Output(BASEADDRESS, ledState);
```

222

//Button3 (bit2) ctc.

Note the AND and the OR logic commands turn the individual bits on and off without affecting the other bits. Add the code for the rest of the buttons. The other off/on values are:

Bit	OFF	ON
2	0xFB	0x04
3	0xF7	0x08
4	0xEF	0x10
5	0xDF	0x20
6	0xBF	0x40
7	0x7F	0x80

This code looks very inefficient to me and I'm sure there's a really neat way of doing it, but it works.

Plug in your LED display and run the program. You should be able to switch the LEDs on and off from the program.

19.8   Oscilloscope application

Let's bring all this together and see how we might interface to an analogue to digital converter and make our PC into an oscilloscope. This could be extended to add Fourier Transform code to produce a frequency display. This example also shows how we can input from the parallel port.

19.8.1 Hardware interface.

Let's suppose we only have a few millivolts as our input from say, a microphone. The signal needs to be amplified and converted to a digital signal for the PC. For this example an analogue to digital (A to D) converter will be used and interfaced through the parallel port. This design uses the Texas Instruments TLC548, 8-bit A to D chip which performs a conversion in 17µs allowing data transfers of up to 45,500 conversions per second. The TLC548 is controlled using three signals, Chip Select (CS) and I/O clock are input control signals and a Data Out signal provides the (serial) digital output.

19.8.2 Amplifier

The TLC 548 analogue input signal level is between 0 Volts and the supply voltage, nominally 5 Volts. Consequently, the microphone signal must be amplified by a few hundred to provide a voltage change at the A to D input of a few volts. In this design both the 741 op-amp used as an amplifier and the A to D converter are run from the same supply voltage of 5 volts, which means that the voltage output from the op-amp will be approximately between 1 and 4 volts. A better design would be to use a separate (and larger) supply for the A to D to provide a wider voltage output range and some isolation between the analogue and digital parts of the circuit.

The amplifier circuit is shown in figure 19.3.

The 100kΩ resistors bias the input signal at ½ the supply voltage, and the gain is approximately 220 (220k / 1k). Thus for a signal of 20mV, the output voltage swing is $20*10^{-3} * 220$, or 4.4 volts.

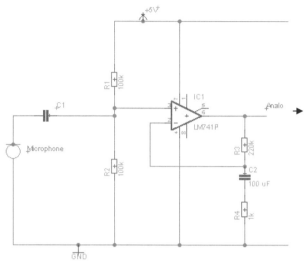

Figure 19.3 Amplifier circuit

19.8.3 Analogue to Digital converter.

The signal from the amplifier goes to the Analog In signal of the TLC548. There are two reference voltages REF+ and REF- which are connected to V_{CC} and 0 Volts respectively. The I/O clock, Chip select and Data Out signal connect directly to the parallel port of the PC.

The A to D circuit is shown in figure 19.4.

224

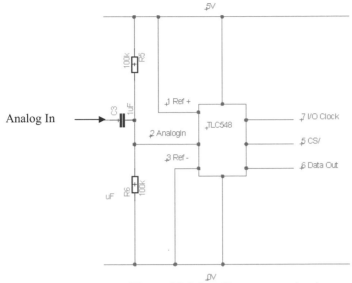

Figure 19.4 A to D converter circuit

We shall use the parallel port as shown in Table 19.3.

Signal Name	Parallel port	Register	Port address	Direction
DATA OUT	Pin 1	Control Register Bit 0	Base address + 2	To PC
I/O CLOCK	Pin 2	Data Register Bit 0	Base address	From PC
CS/	Pin 3	Data Register Bit 1	Base address	From PC

Table 19.3 Parallel port connections

19.8.4 Timing Diagram

The TLC548 provides an on-chip system clock which runs at typically 4MHz and needs no external components. A to D conversion can proceed independently of the serial I/O. The serial I/O timing sequence is as follows:

1. The device is selected by taking CS/ to logic 0. The TLC548 places the most significant data bit (A7) on the DATA OUT line after a maximum of 1.4 μs.
2. The I/O CLOCK signal is pulsed to clock the remaining data bits (A6-A0) on to the DATA OUT bus on the falling edge of I/O CLOCK.
3. The TLC548 initiates the next conversion cycle on the 8th I/O CLOCK pulse; this takes 17 μs. CS/ is taken to logic 1. When the conversion is complete, the cycle can then repeat.

The timing sequence is shown in figure 19.5. More accurate information can be found in the TLC548 data sheet.

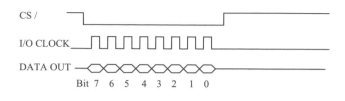

Figure 19.5 Timing diagram

19.8.5 The Oscilloscope Program

The data from the A to D converter is read one bit at a time and formed into a byte. The TLC548 is selected and the program waits about 1.4 µs for the first data bit (bit 7) to be placed on the DATA OUT line. The program then loops eight times reading the DATA OUT line one bit at a time.

The data read from the parallel port is inverted, so the data bit 0 read into 'temp' is inverted. (this is done by checking if the byte read is odd or even using the code:

```
if (temp % 2) == 0))
```

This value is shifted into the result byte 'data'. Whilst this is being done the I/O CLOCK signal is set high and then low. Any bits already read into 'data' are shifted left and the least significant bit of 'temp' is selected using the AND command. Finally the bit in 'temp' is transferred to 'data' using the OR command.

The Performance Counter is used in this design. The program displays the parameters for this when it starts and the number of counts required for 1µs, see figure 19.6.

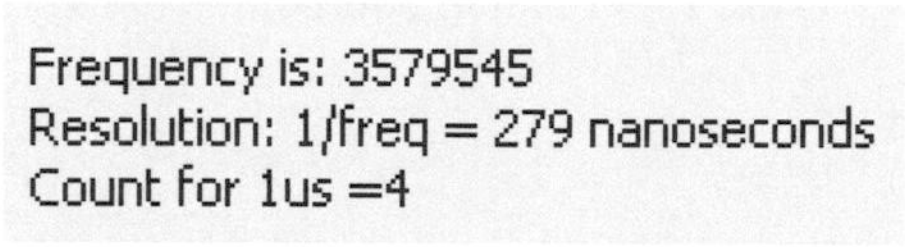

```
Frequency is: 3579545
Resolution: 1/freq = 279 nanoseconds
Count for 1us =4
```

Figure 19.6 Performance counter information

It also displays the time taken to read the 500 samples taken. In my case this is 93ms.

The program displays the graph on a panel (pnlScope) and has an 'Acquire' button (btnAcquire). The panel's paint method is changed to call the DrawGraph method, so the graph is redrawn if it is resized.

The complete code for the oscilloscope follows. Don't forget put the inpout32.dll in the debug folder and add the following declaration at the top of the code:

```
using System.Runtime.InteropServices;
```

Hopefully the code commented well enough for you to follow. The program runs for the frequency of my PC, so may have to be modified for your PC. Figure 19.7 shows the display output.

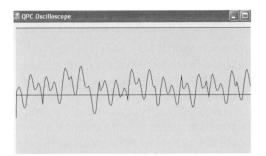

Figure 19.7 Oscilloscope display

```
namespace QPCOscilloscope
{
    public partial class Form1 : Form
    {
        [DllImport("kernel32.dll")]
        extern static short QueryPerformanceCounter(ref long x);
        [DllImport("kernel32.dll")]
        extern static short QueryPerformanceFrequency(ref long x);
        [DllImport("inpout32.dll", EntryPoint = "Out32")]
        public static extern void Output(int address, int value);
        [DllImport("inpout32.dll", EntryPoint = "Inp32")]
        public static extern int Input(int address);

        const int PARPORT = 0x378;
        int data = 0;     // data read from port
        int[] dataArray;
        public System.Drawing.Graphics grpObject;
        // values for Performance Counter
        long counter = 0, counter1=0, freq = 0;
        long microSecCount = 0, resolution =0;

        public Form1()
        {
            InitializeComponent();
            dataArray = new int[500];
            grpObject = this.pnlScope.CreateGraphics();
        }

        private void calibrate()
        {
```

```csharp
        // read frequency counter,
        // and calculate how many counter ticks are needed for 1us
        // find out QP frequency of PC
        if (QueryPerformanceCounter(ref counter) != 0)
            // Begin timing.
        {
            QueryPerformanceFrequency(ref freq);
            resolution = (int)1000000000 / freq;        // in nanoseconds
            microSecCount = 1+ (1000/resolution);       // or round up
            // debug message
            MessageBox.Show("Frequency is: " + freq + "\r\n" +
                "Resolution: 1/freq = " + resolution + " nanoseconds\r\n"+
                "Count for 1us =" + microSecCount);
            // count for 1us  = 1000/resolution
        }
    }

    private void btnAcquire_Click(object sender, EventArgs e)
    {
        btnAcquire.Enabled = false;
        DateTime dtTimeIt = new DateTime();
        dtTimeIt = DateTime.Now;
        int temp;
        pnlScope.Width = 500;
        pnlScope.Height = 280;

        /*************
        Printer port is at 0x378,
        Data register: bit 0 (at 0x378) = I/O CLOCK, pin 2 of 'D' type
                    bit 1 = CS/, pin 3 of 'D' connector.
        Control reg. is at 0x37a (base + 2),
                    bit0/ = DATA OUT, pin 1 of 'D' type
        *************/

        // get samples
        for (int samples = 0; samples < 500; samples++)
        {
            Output(PARPORT, 0);   //cs low, I/O clock low
                // wait 1.4us before data is ready to send
            delay(2);
            data = 0;                   // holds data formed from the serial bits
            for (int i = 1; i < 9; i++)
            {
                // 8 times - read bit control port (base+2), bit 0
                temp = Input(PARPORT + 2);
                // bit0 is inverted
```

```csharp
            if ((temp % 2) == 0) temp = 1;  // was 0, set it
            else temp = 0;                  // was 1, clear 0
            // clock the I/O clock
            Output(PARPORT, 1);      // clock high
            data = data << 1;        // get data whilst waiting for clock
            temp = temp & 1;         // get ls bit only
            Output(PARPORT, 0);      // clock low
            data = data | temp;      // bit now in data
        }                            // end of for i = 1 to <9
        Output(PARPORT, 2);          // reset CS, bit 1 high to start
        dataArray[samples] = data;

        delay(17);                              // delay 17us
    }              // end of for i = 1 to 500 samples

    TimeSpan tspan = DateTime.Now - dtTimeIt;

    btnAcquire.Enabled = true;
    // debug message
    MessageBox.Show("500 samples in " +
        tspan.Milliseconds.ToString() + " ms");
    // my laptop does 500 samples in 93ms.
    // 186 us per sample, 5.4kHz

    pnlScope.Invalidate();       // force redraw
    //DrawGraph();
}

private void DrawGraph()
{
    int x = 0, y = 0;
    // clear panel
    grpObject.Clear(Color.LightGray);
    // draw some grid lines
    Pen objmyPen = new Pen(System.Drawing.Color.Blue);
    // draw 0 V grid line
    grpObject.DrawLine(objmyPen, 0, pnlScope.Height,
        pnlScope.Width,pnlScope.Height);
    // draw 2.5 Volt grid line
    grpObject.DrawLine(objmyPen, 0, pnlScope.Height / 2,
        pnlScope.Width, pnlScope.Height / 2);
    // draw 5 V line
    grpObject.DrawLine(objmyPen, 0, 0, pnlScope.Width, 0);

    for (int count = 0; count < 500; count++)
    {
```

```csharp
        if (count != 0)      // don't draw first point, just save it
        {
            //          {draw line }
            grpObject.DrawLine(objmyPen, x, y, count,
                    255 - dataArray[count]);
        }
        x = count;
        y = 255 - dataArray[count];
    } // end count loop
}

private void Form1_Load(object sender, EventArgs e)
{
    // Set CS/ low(selecting the TLC548) and I/O CLOCK low}
    Output(PARPORT,0);
    data = 0;       // clear result byte 'data'
                    // freq holds frequency of counter
                    // read PC frequency and set resolution
    calibrate();
}

private void delay(int delayTime)
{
    // pass integer value indicating required delay time in 1 us
    // there are 2 required for this program 1.4us (pass 2)
    // and 17us (pass 17)
    //
    // read counter
    QueryPerformanceCounter(ref counter);        // Start timing.
    // and loop while count is less than required
    //
    // Read counter again to set finish counter
    QueryPerformanceCounter(ref counter1);
    while ((counter1-counter)<(delayTime*microSecCount))
    {
        QueryPerformanceCounter(ref counter1);    // read again
    }
}

private void pnlScope_Paint(object sender, PaintEventArgs e)
{
    DrawGraph();
}
    }
}
```

Self Assessment Exercises

1. Connect to PCs with a null-modem serial cable (one with pins 2 and 3 crossed over) and write a chat program so that users on two separate PCs can communicate.

2. Extend this program so that files can be transferred between the PCs.

3. Connect some parallel outputs to inputs and write a program to set the outputs and read the inputs. Remember only some parallel port bits are guaranteed to be inputs.

4. Connect some switches to the parallel port and write a program to read the state of the switches. You will have to check which lines are capable of input.

5. Find out the resolution of your PC using the Performance frequency and counter (see previous chapter) and calibrate the oscilloscope program for your PC.

6. Add graph scales to the oscilloscope program. Calculate these from your sampling rate.

7. Use NPlot to draw the graph.

8. Drive the oscilloscope program from a signal generator and compare results with those expected.

Summary

In this chapter we have covered interfacing with the serial and parallel ports. The former using the SerialPort toolbox control and the latter using an external DLL. A simple parallel output design driving LEDs was studied. A more detailed hardware and software design to use the PC as an oscilloscope followed. This used the PC performance counter to speed up the operation. In the next chapter we shall look at interfacing the PC using the USB port.

20   USB interfacing

20.1   Introduction

The USB port is now the most popular way of interfacing peripherals to the PC. A complete USB design involves designing the USB product hardware as well as software for the product itself and drivers for the PC.

Many manufacturers make USB products you can program with your code (e.g. Cypress, Velleman and Microchip PIC products).But if you want a simple interface, integrated circuits are available which provide a direct USB to serial and USB to parallel interface, for example the FT232R and FT245R devices from Future Technology Devices International (FTDI).

You can of course design using the available integrated circuits which have an USB interface, but for evaluation there is an easier way. DLP Design Inc. (www.dlpdesign.com) manufacture a USB/Microcontroller module which uses the FT245R device. The module is the DLP-245PB-G and we shall study a design using this device. This not only provides a USB to parallel interface and all the drivers we need, for both PC and USB ends, but also contains a Microchip PIC microcontroller which can be also programmed for your application. DLP Design also make a similar module which incorporates the serial FT232R serial device.

20.2   The USB interface

We do not need to know much about the USB interface to get the module design working, so we shall not cover the USB interface in detail here. Suffice it to say, the USB consortium (www.usb.org) governs the protocol and standards of USB. Whilst anyone can make a USB product, it cannot display the 'USB Certified' logo without the consortium evaluating it. They will provide you with a unique vendor ID (VID). You can either register your own VID for $2000 or you can use FTDI's for free. For more information, refer to: http://www.dlpdesign.com/usb-prev/vid.shtml.

USB version 2.0 specifies three modes of operation: High speed (480 Mbits/s), Full speed (12 Mbits/s) and Low speed (1.5 Mbits/s). The USB interface uses four wires, two for power and two data lines called D+ and D-. The device itself indicates its presence and speed by pulling either the D+ or D- data line high.

Your device can take its power from the USB bus but if so, stringent rules must be met.

The host (i.e. your PC) controls the USB bus and initiates and controls all messages to the slaves. There can be up to 127 devices on the bus and hence a device may not run at its maximum speed.

The USB connectors come in a few limited types. The standard A-type is exclusively for a host (e.g. your PC) and the B-types are for connection to slaves. These can be seen in figure 20.1. There are also smaller Micro A and B-types which are available for small devices such as PDAs, phones and digital cameras.

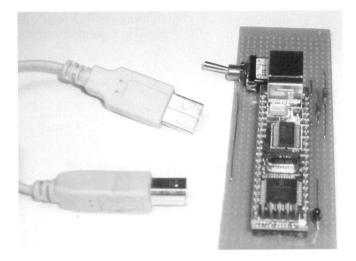

Figure 20.1 DLP-245PB-G module.

20.3   USB Module installation and hardware

We will create a USB design using the DLP Design's DLP-245PB-G module. DLP Design is based in Allen, Texas and FTDI are one of their distributors in the UK. Figure 20.1 shows the device with an LED and switch attached for our program example.

The module features:

- USB 1.0 and 2.0 compatible – communication at up to 2Mbits/s
- 18 digital I/O lines (6 as A/D inputs)
- Programmable Microchip 16F877A PIC
- Pre-programmed code to interface to USB providing access to the I/O, EEPROM and external digital temperature sensors
- Access to the PIC data bus for further expansion.

More importantly no in-depth knowledge of USB hardware or software is required, only an understanding of the communication protocol. The module also has the advantage of being in a 40-pin DIL pin-out, so further expansion is easy.

More information can be found at www.ftdichip.com/Documents/DataSheets/DLP/dlp-245pbv20.pdf

20.3.1 Installing the drivers

The combined driver module (CDM) D2XX drivers must be downloaded and extracted from the FTDI web site at: http://www.ftdichip.com/Drivers/D2XX.htm. This enables access through either D2XX DLL or via COM port. The current version is 2.04.06 (March 13, 2008)

Follow the installation instructions at:
http://www.dlpdesign.com/winXP_install_guide.pdf.

Having installed the drivers, you can check the device in Control Panel's Device Manager, USB Controllers. See figure 20.2.

Figure 20.2 USB Properties

The VID and PID can be seen in the details tab, but we won't need to know or use them:

Figure 20.3 VID and PID

To see if your module works, you can try the loopback example (number 3) at www.ftdichip.com/Projects/CodeExamples/CSharp.htm.
Although this is for the serial version, it does detect the device and shows its properties. Running it reported the following for my module:

    Device Index: 0
    Flags: 0
    Type: FT_DEVICE_232R
    ID: 4036001
    Location ID: 11
    Serial Number: DPCXXHCN

Description: DLP-245PB

Further example software is available on purchase of the module.

20.3.2 The DLL communication software

Programs communicate with the module using the .NET class FTD2XX_NET. Download this from the FDTI web site and extract it. It needs to be added to References in Solution Explorer for every program you write. I suggest you put a copy of the DLL and XML file in the program's folder. To add the reference right-click References and Browse for the file FTD2XX_NET.DLL. This provides commands such as Read and Write so we can communicate with the module. The XML file provides information to the IntelliSense so we can see the methods and their descriptions, see figure 20.4.

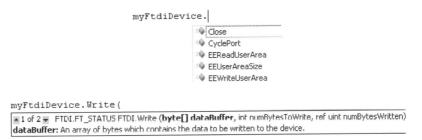

Figure 20.4 IntelliSense FTD2XX_NET DLL display

Detailed information on these can be found in the D2XX_Programmer's_Guide at the FDTI web site.

20.3.4 The hardware design.

There is little to do as far as the hardware is concerned. A link needs to be made from pin 20 to pin 19 if you wish to power the module from the USB bus and obviously any connections need to be made to the inputs and outputs that you need. Figure 20.5 shows the top-view pin out and the pin descriptions are shown in Table 20.1.

Pin #	Description	Pin #	Description
1	Ground	40	Ground
2	E0 – I/O pin A/D channel 5	39	C7 – (I/O) port pin C7
3	A0 – I/O pin A/D channel 0	38	C6 – (I/O) port pin C6
4	A1 – I/O pin A/D channel 1	37	C5 – (I/O) port pin C5
5	A2 – I/O pin A/D channel 2	36	C4 – (I/O) port pin C4
6	A3 – I/O pin A/D channel 3	35	C3 – (I/O) port pin C3
7	A4 – I/O pin open drain output	34	C2 – (I/O) port pin C2
8	A5 – I/O pin A/D channel 4	33	C1 – (I/O) port pin C1
9	UPRST (in) - Reset input	32	C0 – (I/O) port pin C0
10	Ground	31	B0 – (I/O) port pin B0

11	Reset# (in) - ext. reset	30	B4 – (I/O) port pin B4
12	N/C	29	B5 – (I/O) port pin B5
13	Ground	28	DB0 – data bus 0
14	3V3OUT (out) - 3.3V output (max 5mA)	27	DB1 – data bus 1
15	Ground	26	DB2 – data bus 2
16	SWVCC (out)	25	DB3 – data bus 3
17	Ground	24	DB4 – data bus 4
18	N/C	23	DB5 – data bus 5
19	EXTVCC (in) - 5V input	22	DB6 – data bus 6
20	PORTVCC (out) - connect to pin 19 for USB powered designs	21	DB7 – data bus 7

Table 20.1 Pin descriptions

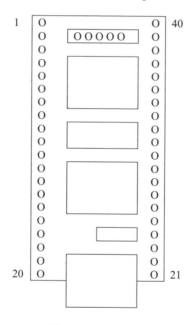

Figure 20.5 Pin out

The 5-pin connector on the device is used for programming the PIC.

In this design the module is powered by the USB interface. Connect pin 20 to pin 19 (PORTVCC (out) to EXTVCC (in)).

For the output, connect an LED and resistor to pin 2 (port E bit 0).
For the input, connect a switch and resistor to pin 32 (port C bit 0).

Once the software drivers are loaded, connect it with a USB cable. It should be recognised by Windows.

20.3.5 Communications Protocol

To communicate with the device a number of bytes is sent:

1. The number of bytes in the command and data, excluding the checksum
2. Command
3. Data or parameters
4. CheckSum – an ExclusiveOR of the previous bytes

The device responds with a 0x55 if the checksum agrees, or 0xAA if not. This has to be read by the host PC. If you have requested data, you then read the data.

If you perform too many reads, the device will hang.

Example:
To read port D the following commands are sent:
1. 0x01   One byte command
2. 0x5B   Read port D
3. 0x5A   (0x01 EXOR 0x5B)

The response will be a 0x55 (checksum match), followed by the data from port D. Two reads of the module have to be made.

To write 0x24 to port D the following commands are sent:
1. 0x02   Two byte command
2. 0x5C   Write to port D
3. 0x24   Data
4. 0x7A   (0x02 EXOR 0x5C EXOR 24)

The response will be a 0x55 (checksum match). This has to be read.

20.4   USB Module Software

Let's write a program initially to detect the device on the USB port and extend this to toggle bit 0 of port E and then reads port C. Note this code is designed for only one module only on the USB port.

Start a new project.
Add the following at the top of the code:

```
using System.Threading;
using FTD2XX_NET;
```

Add FTD2XX_NET to the References. (Right-click and browse)

We will now add all the declarations we will need. Add the following before the code public Form1( ):

```
// Create new instance of the FTDI device class
FTDI myFtdiDevice = new FTDI();
FTDI.FT_STATUS ftStatus = FTDI.FT_STATUS.FT_OK;
UInt32 numBytesWritten = 0;
UInt32 numBytesToRead = 1;
UInt32 numBytesRead=0;
byte[ ] dataBytes = new byte[5];
```

Let's see if the device is present by seeing how many there are:
Add the following to the Form load event:

```
UInt32 ftdiDevCount = 0;

// How many?
ftStatus = myFtdiDevice.GetNumberOfDevices(ref ftdiDevCount);
// Check status
if (ftStatus == FTDI.FT_STATUS.FT_OK)
  {
    MessageBox.Show("Number of FTDI devices: " +
        ftdiDevCount.ToString());
  }
else
  {
    MessageBox.Show("Failed to get number of devices: Error " +
        ftStatus.ToString());
  }

// Allocate storage for device info list
FTDI.FT_DEVICE_INFO_NODE[ ] ftdiDeviceList = new
FTDI.FT_DEVICE_INFO_NODE[ftdiDevCount];

// Populate the device list
ftStatus = myFtdiDevice.GetDeviceList(ftdiDeviceList);

// Open first device in our list by serial number – hopefully there's only one
ftStatus =
myFtdiDevice.OpenBySerialNumber(ftdiDeviceList[0].SerialNumber);
if (ftStatus != FTDI.FT_STATUS.FT_OK)
{
    MessageBox.Show("Failed to open device: Error " +
        ftStatus.ToString());
}
```

If you've added the Windows drivers, connect the module using a USB cable and run the program to see if it's working. You should get a message as shown in figure 20.6.

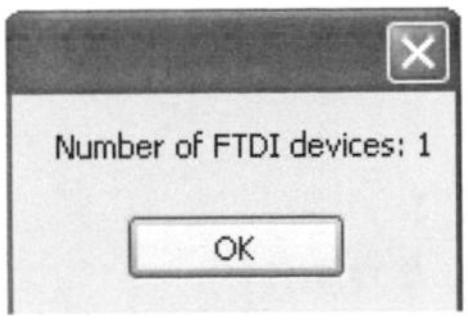

Figure 20.6 FTDI detect message

20.4.1 Setting outputs

Now let's extend the program to toggle output port E, bit 0 (pin 2). You can connect an LED to this pin to see the program working. To set and reset this bit the command sequence is:

1. 0x03   Three byte command
2. 0xA6   Set port pin
3. 0x48   Port pin is E0
4. 0x01   Set the bit (0 for reset)
5. 0xEC   EXOR of previous bytes – 0xED for reset

After the code: FTDI myFtdiDevice = new FTDI(); add the code:

```
// record E0 bit state
int e0State=0;
```

Add a button to the form and for the button click code type the following:

```
// Toggle E0 pin

// To set E0 command bytes are:
// 0x03, 0xA6, 0x48, 0x01, 0xEC
// 0x03 XOR 0xA6 XOR 0x48 XOR 0x01 = 0xEC.
// and to reset E0 command is:
// 0x03, 0xA6, 0x48, 0x00, 0xED

dataBytes[0] = 0x03;    // 3 bytes (not including CS)
dataBytes[1] = 0xA6;    // set port pin
dataBytes[2] = 0x48;    // 0x48 = port E, bit 0

if (e0State==0)
{
    // then set
    e0State = 1;
    dataBytes[3] = 0x01;    // set bit
    dataBytes[4] = 0xEC;    // CS
}
```

239

```
    else
    {
      // reset
      e0State = 0;
      dataBytes[3] = 0x00;   // reset bit
      dataBytes[4] = 0xED;   // CS
    }

    // And write data to the device
    ftStatus = myFtdiDevice.Write
          (dataBytes, dataBytes.Length, ref numBytesWritten);
    if (ftStatus != FTDI.FT_STATUS.FT_OK)
    {
        MessageBox.Show("Failed getting bytes: Error " + ftStatus.ToString());
    }
    // else OK

    // read the CS message
    myFtdiDevice.Read(dataBytes, numBytesToRead, ref numBytesRead);
    if (dataBytes[0] == 0xAA)
    {
      MessageBox.Show("Checksum error");
    }
```

Try the program. The port output should switch on and off.

20.4.2 Reading Inputs

We can now try to read port C. The command sequence for this is:

1. 0x01   One byte command
2. 0x59   Read port C
3. 0x58   (0x01 EXOR 0x59)

The Write command sends a byte array or string. The checksum response is read first, followed by the data.

Add a button and the following code for the button click event:

```
    // Write byte array data
    dataBytes[0] = 0x01;          // one byte command
    dataBytes[1] = 0x59;          // Read port C
    dataBytes[2] = 0x58;          // CS = 1 xor 59

    // send the command
    ftStatus = myFtdiDevice.Write(dataBytes, dataBytes.Length,
          ref numBytesWritten);
```

```
if (ftStatus != FTDI.FT_STATUS.FT_OK)
{
   MessageBox.Show("Failed to write to device
      (error " + ftStatus.ToString() + ")");
}

// read response - 0xAA (170) indicates CS error, 0x55 (85) is OK
// this has to be read from the buffer.
numBytesToRead =1;
myFtdiDevice.Read(dataBytes, numBytesToRead, ref numBytesRead);
if (dataBytes[0] == 0xAA)
{
   // CS error
   MessageBox.Show("CS Error");
}
else
{
   //no CS error - read data
   numBytesToRead = 1;
   myFtdiDevice.Read(dataBytes, numBytesToRead, ref numBytesRead);
   // and display port C state
   MessageBox.Show("Port C0 = " + dataBytes[0].ToString());
}
```

The port data should be shown as in figure 20.7. Note that if the inputs are floating, their values may be indeterminant.

Figure 20.7 Port C display

Now that you know how to read and write to the ports, you can do anything. In addition though, the module has capability of connecting to analogue devices and a temperature sensor. The commands to do this are described in the manual.

You can also find out how to program the PIC to run programs for you.

Self Assessment Exercises

1. Design a program to read and write to all the ports.

2. Write a program to read an analogue input. Either read the output set by the previous program or add a potentiometer to supply an analogue input to the module and read it.

3. The module supports commands to communicate with a Maxim DS18S20-PAR one-wire interface digital thermometer. Connect one of these to the module and write a program to read and display the temperature.

4. Write a program to generate a PWM (pulse width modulated) output signal. This can be turned into an analogue output if passed through an RC low pass filter.

5. The module contains a programmable PIC. Program this to run its own program and send data to the PC. For more information on this see the DLP design's documentation.

Summary

In this chapter we have briefly looked at the USB port. We have seen how the DLP designs DLP245PB-G module can be connected to a PC using their USB drivers. We have seen in detail how to communicate with the module and read and write to the ports, providing digital I/O and analogue input.

21 Conclusion

The idea behind this book was to enable you to understand the .NET environment and programming in C#, ultimately to interface your hardware to a PC and provide a useful user interface for your designs.

In doing so it has covered a lot of ground; from the software aspects of the .NET framework and libraries, the C# programming language; file handling; threading and internet communication, through to graphical interfacing and database handling and on to hardware interfacing using the serial port control, using an external DLL to drive the parallel port and the USB port, finally producing a complete USB design.

I hope that the book has provided enough to get you going, that the examples have been clear and that it has spurred you on to with your own designs.

Of course there is still a lot more you can learn, from more detailed Object Oriented Programming such as polymorphism and delegates; advanced relational databases and searching with LINQ; to XML and Web Services, as well as further hardware USB interfacing.

I hope that this book has given you the background and confidence to discover these for yourself. I wish you all the best in your designs.

Index

Structured Query Language, 185
Structures, 60
subtract
    operator, 51
switch statement, 73

—T—

TabControl, 36
TabIndex, 34
TCP. *See* Transmission Control Protocol
TCP client, 152
TCP server, 151
Text, 28, 30
TextBox, 28
TextChanged, 29
thread states, 141
Threading, 141
throw statement, 80
Timer, 43
Toolbox, 18
ToString method, 98
Transmission Control Protocol, 150
Trim, 64
try-catch, 79

—U—

UDP. *See* User Datagram Protocol
UDP communications, 158
UDPClient.Receive, 159
UDPClient.Send, 159
Unsafe code, 213
upper case, 65
USB
    driver, 234
    module, 233
    module hardware, 235
    module software, 237
USB port, 232
User Datagram Protocol, 150

—V—

Video support, 26
virtual
    keyword, 104

—W—

while statement, 77

—X—

XOR, 53